Practising Shiatsu

MIND · BODY · AND SPIRIT

**GEDDES &
GROSSET**

Warning

Shiatsu should never be used in place of medical treatment and care.

You should never stop taking or reduce any medication without the approval of your doctor.

Consult your doctor before starting any course of shiatsu treatment.

This edition published 2002 by Geddes & Grosset,
David Dale House, New Lanark ML11 9DJ, Scotland

© 1999 Geddes & Grosset

First published 1999
Reprinted 1999, 2002

Cover photograph by Tom Paddington courtesy of the Stock Market

ISBN 1 85534 367 3

Printed and bound in the UK

Contents

Introduction

Origins

It is thought that shiatsu originated in China at least 2000 years ago, when the earliest accounts gave the causes of ailments and the remedies that could be effected through a change of diet and way of life. The use of massage and acupuncture was also recommended. With time, a variety of techniques and information was gathered and eventually the practice was developed in Japan. The Japanese practised this particular technique of massage, after it had been introduced into their country, and it was known as anma or amma, ancient oriental massage. The therapy that is known today as shiatsu has gradually evolved with time from anma under influences from both East and West and is a mixture of ancient massage, self-massage (also called Do-In) and some features of judo. It is only very recently that it has gained recognition and popularity, with people becoming aware of its existence and benefits. The word shiatsu itself derives from shi which means fingers and atsu which means pressure. The technique is thus self-explanatory from its name, applying pressure to parts of the body using the fingers. However, as may be expected, there is much more to shiatsu than this and recent developments do not merely utilise the fingers.

The constituent practice, anma, is a similar technique in which parts of the body are pressed and rubbed. This was a recognised practice around the 7th and 8th centuries AD in China and after phases where it was in and out of fashion, in the late 18th century a detailed book on the subject was produced. The underlying principle of this technique was that of meridians, or channels of energy and pressure points – both of which are familiar ideas today. Interestingly, many of the early practitioners of anma were blind. The western input into shiatsu of massage can be traced back a very long way and it was certainly mentioned at the time of Hippocrates, several hundred years BC.

Although East and West have different viewpoints on health and life, these can complement one another. The Eastern belief is of a primary flow of energy throughout the body, which runs along certain channels known as meridians. It is also believed that this energy exists throughout the universe and that all living creatures are dependent upon it as much as on physical nourishment. The energy is known by three similar names, ki (or qi), chi and prana in Japan, China and India respectively.

(It should be noted that the term 'energy' in this context is not the same as the physical quantity that is measured in joules or calories.) As in acupuncture, there are certain pressure points on the meridians that relate to certain organs, and these points are known as tsubos.

Shiatsu today combines elements of these practices and also may combine applications or routines from additional therapies such as chiropractic. The core practical procedure is that a controlled pressure is applied to a part of the body by pressing, rubbing, rolling, pinching, patting, rotating, etc. The body will naturally respond to these stimuli and the therapist will then apply corresponding stimulation. This direct application of pressure encourages within the body the proper circulation of the body fluids and functioning of the organs.

The applications of shiatsu

As a result of its long lineage and combined with other therapies that utilise massage, shiatsu has been found to be effective in curing or alleviating the symptoms of many conditions. Shiatsu can be used to treat a variety of minor problems and others which many (especially the sufferers) would consider quite major. These include:

• insomnia
• headaches
• anxiety

- back pain
- fatigue
- poor circulation
- weight problems
- indigestion
- chills and flushes
- poor appetite
- helping in chronic cases of rheumatism
- high blood pressure

In Japan, shiatsu is used commonly for minor conditions and diseases and is an important component of good health practice.

Western medicine may be unable to find a physical cause for a problem, and although some pain relief may be provided, the underlying cause of the problem may not be cured. It is possible that one session of shiatsu will be sufficient to remedy the problem by stimulating the flow of energy along the channels. A regime of exercise (possibly a specific routine) with a change in diet and/or lifestyle may also be recommended. Shiatsu can encourage a general feeling of good health in the whole person, not just in the physical sense. After some study or practice, shiatsu can be performed on friends and relatives. There are many benefits for both the giver and the receiver of shiatsu, both on a physical and spiritual level.

Although shiatsu is essentially undertaken using the

fingers, there are alternative schools which have developed other techniques, notably the barefoot shiatsu style, created by Suzuki Yamamoto. This technique, where the practitioner stands on certain areas of the body (back, legs and feet) was developed to deal specifically with what became known as 'the Western condition'. This was a reference to the solid appearance of individuals who had taken in substantial amounts of animal food in their diet. Alternatively named macrobiotic, this technique combined the shiatsu with stretching, exercises for breathing, and dietary recommendations to provide a holistic approach, thereby achieving a balance. Whenever problems are experienced, an answer can be sought in the imbalance within one or more aspects of life, whether it be diet, movement, thought, etc, and in ancient Chinese healing, the ever changing balance of yin and yang, complementary yet opposing, were used.

Yin and Yang

Yin and yang are the be all and end all: the cause of life and death. The Chinese equate the earth, or creation with yin and the sky or heaven with yang. Pictorially, yin is represented by a line of two dashes while yang is a continuous line, each derived from the square and circle which in turn represent the earth and heaven, respectively. The origin of this lies with the fact that yin and yang lines were used as ancient oracles. Oracles of ancient times gave a yes or no answer to any question put to them and yes was represented by the yang, unbroken, line and yin, no, by the broken line.

Yin and yang are inextricably linked because, while yin is restful and yang is active, activity invariably ends with rest and likewise rest leads to further activity. The activity of yang ends with the inactivity of yin. This is graphically shown in the well known symbol for yin and yang which is often called the T'ai ch'i, something quite different from the system of exercise for which the full name is T'ai chi chu'an.

Although yin and yang are effectively opposites, together they produce a balance and within each there is

Figure 1 – yin and yang

some part of the other, represented in the symbol by the dot of contrasting colour – white in black and black in white (*see* figure 1). They are thus opposites and, from traditional beliefs, it was thought that interactions between them formed all manner of occurrences in nature and the whole of the world and beyond. Yin and yang and their negative/positive aspects also relate to the individual, the home and his or her occupation. A number of characteristics or properties can be attributed to yin or yang and in turn the physical makeup of a person will be one or the other. The table on page 14 shows some typical properties. It also shows the movements and ac-

tivities, so central to shiatsu, and some body functions
that fall into yin or yang.

Yin	Yang
Earth	Sky
Creation	Heaven
Winter	Summer
Dark	Bright
Cold	Warm
Night	Day
Water	Fire
Down	Up
North	South
Female	Male
Inner	Outer
Passive	Active
Negative	Positive
Receptive	Creative
Moving up	Moving down
Relaxing	Tensing
Slow	Quick
Mental activity	Physical activity
Elimination (in the body)	Consumption (in the body)
Extremities of the body	Inner parts of the body
Body front	Body back
Pliable	Rigid

Yin and yang are always interconnected and there is a state of constant flux between the two which nevertheless creates an overall state of balance.

As previously mentioned, diet is important and a change may be recommended by a shiatsu practitioner. From the viewpoint of traditional Oriental medicine, food can be defined in an 'energetic' way. This differs from the Western definition of foods consisting of protein, minerals, fats, carbohydrates, fibre and vitamins. It is believed that, according to its 'energetic' definition, food will have differing physical, mental, spiritual and emotional effects. This energy is split into the two parts – yin and yang. Yin is where energy is expanding and yang, where it is contracting. In this context, all definitions of yin and yang are based on macrobiotic food (a diet intended to prolong life, comprised of pure vegetable foods such as brown rice), this being the most usual reference. Food can be divided into three main types: those that are 'balanced', and some that are yin and some that are yang.

Foods that are defined as being yin are: milk, alcohol, honey, sugar, oil, fruit juices, spices, stimulants, most drugs (such as aspirin, etc), tropical vegetables and fruits, refined foods, and most food additives of a chemical nature.

Yang foods are poultry, seafood, eggs, meat, salt, fish, miso and cheese.

Balanced foods are seeds, nuts, vegetables, cereal grains, beans, sea vegetables and temperate fruits (such as apples and pears).

The balance between yin and yang is very important to the body, for example, in the production of hormones such as oestrogen and progesterone, and glycogen and insulin and the expansion and contraction of the lungs, etc. A 'balanced' way of eating, mainly from the grains, beans, seeds, nuts and vegetables, etc., is important as this will help to achieve the energy balance in the meridians, organs and chakras, as defined elsewhere. When these two opposing forces of yin and yang are in harmony and balanced, physical and mental health will result.

The Importance of Diet

It is often stated that 'you are what you eat' and in recent years there has been an avalanche of information, much of it conflicting, about what constitutes a healthy diet. In many cases, this has caused a great deal of confusion and has led to the feeling in the mind of a suspicious public that every food, particularly if you enjoy eating it, is bad for you! In order to clarify the picture, it is worthwhile examining the role of different types of food in the human body. In many instances, it is not a particular food that is the villain, but what may have happened to it during its growth or processing. A range of chemicals and additives come into this category (and there have been many health scares concerning them), and also possible contamination by food poisoning organisms. Unless you are in the fortunate position of being able to follow your food from the field or garden to the table, the most that can be achieved is to keep well-informed, follow sensible guidelines and to make the best choices possible.

The human body requires food to provide energy for all life processes and for growth, repair and maintenance of cells and tissues. In general, men require more food than women due to their larger body size, but needs differ according to age and level of activity. Young active people require more food than those who are elderly and more sedentary but, in addition, slight internal differences exist between individuals who may seem outwardly comparable.

There are three main groups of substances – carbohydrates, proteins and fats – contained in food which are needed by the body in differing amounts. (The tables later in the book provide a guide to the content of foods, in calories, fat, fibre and so on.) In addition, the body requires fibre and vitamins and minerals which are present in varying quantities in different types of food. The following provides a brief summary about each with points of particular relevance to shiatsu mentioned.

Carbohydrates

Carbohydrates are organic compounds which may be simple or complex, and their role is to provide an easily utilised source of energy for the body, (measured in calories). All carbohydrates are composed of carbon, hydrogen and oxygen and are manufactured by plants. The simple forms are sugars, of which the most basic is glucose. All carbohydrates are eventually broken down by digestive processes into glucose, which is absorbed and utilised by the body in various ways. With sugars, this process is rapid and the resulting glucose is soon absorbed into the bloodstream. It may be used immediately, particularly if energy demands are high as during vigorous exercise, and athletes often take glucose for this purpose. Glucose is required by red blood cells and is the main source of energy for the brain. Starches are more complex (polysaccharide) carbohydrates built up of chains of glucose molecules. They take longer to be broken down by digestive enzymes than sugars and hence provide a slower, more gradual supply of glucose. The body fluids generally contain enough reserves of glucose to meet the energy requirements for one day's activity. In conditions where there is a lack of available glucose, the body is able to manufacture it in the liver by a biochemical process called gluconeogenesis. Glycerol (from fats) and amino acids (from proteins) are used as raw materials in this process. Conversely, excess glucose is converted by the liver into the complex (polysaccharide) carbohydrate, glycogen (animal starch). This is stored, particularly in liver and muscle cells, and is used first when there is a lack of glucose in the blood.

In general, simple sugars, especially the refined type found in processed foodstuffs e.g. sweets, biscuits, cakes, chocolates, sauces, etc. merely provide the body with calories and are a significant cause of tooth decay. Starches, which are found in a wide range of foods including cereals, grains, bread, pasta, potatoes, vegetables and fruits are far more useful, often having accompanying fibre, vitamins and minerals. However, the levels of these are reduced in starchy foods which are refined and processed, e.g. white varieties of bread, flour, rice and pasta. Many people enjoy the less useful forms of refined sugars and carbohydrates which are easily eaten in excess and contribute towards the problems of tooth decay, weight gain and obesity. There is no need to completely exclude these from the diet but it is sensible to make some simple adjustments towards a more healthy choice of carbohydrates by eating more starch-rich foods. If wholemeal, brown or bran-rich varieties are chosen, this has the added advantage of increasing the fibre content of the diet. Also, these are generally more satisfying and filling, and equally as tasty, as their white counterparts and so help to reduce the desire to eat between meals. These principles are best followed in conjunction with the pursuit of shiatsu. Sugar is considered by many followers to be a poison to the system and should be avoided in a sensible diet.

Proteins
Proteins are the structural components of the body form-

ing the basis of cells, tissues and organs. They are a large group of organic compounds consisting of carbon, hydrogen, nitrogen and oxygen atoms. These are arranged in various ways to form units called amino acids which, when joined together in long chains, make up the structure of the protein. There are 20 basic amino acids which are usually arranged in linear molecules known as polypeptides. Although there are only 20 different kinds, there are a huge number of possible arrangements in a polypeptide or protein, as the amino acids can be in any order. Most proteins consist of more than one polypeptide chain and there are many thousands in the human body, each with a unique structure but all made from the 'pool' of 20 amino acids.

In addition to being structural molecules, proteins are used in the body for storage, as messengers (e.g. hormones), carriers (e.g. the 'globin' in the haemoglobin of the blood which transports oxygen) and as catalysts of biochemical reactions (e.g. enzymes). The body is able to manufacture 12 of the 20 amino acids. However, the remainder, called the 'essential amino acids' must be obtained from the diet. Proteins are widely found in foods derived both from plant and animal sources. Plant sources include beans, peas, pulses, whole grains, nuts and seeds, while red meat, poultry, fish, milk, cheese, yoghurt and eggs are obtained from animals. Red meat is a good source of essential amino acids and iron and was traditionally regarded as 'first class' protein, but the trend now is away from meat to a more vegetarian diet. In shiatsu, the consumption of animal protein is minimised to reduce fat intake (some in addition reduce their intake of dairy products). However, vegetarians can obtain plenty of protein and iron from plant sources and from dairy products. Alternatives to the consumption of red meat include chicken, fish, pulses, beans etc. which are high in protein but low in saturated fat.

Fats

Fats are a group of organic compounds that occur naturally in plant and animal cells in the form of lipids, consisting of carbon, hydrogen and oxygen atoms. Lipids include oils, fats, waxes and related substances, known as 'derived lipids'. A fat consists of one glycerol and three fatty acid molecules, collectively known as a triglyceride and, during digestion, is broken down into its constituent parts by enzymes called lipases. Fats play a vital role in the human body and perform many functions. They are an important energy store, having twice the calorific value (38 cals per gram – *see* the tables later for specific values and details) than carbohydrates. In human beings, fat is deposited in a layer beneath the skin (as subcutaneous fat) where it provides insulation and cushioning. It is also laid down in deeper regions of the body (as adipose tissue) around organs and within cells. Animal fat, including that of man, is solid at room temperature and is of the type known as saturated (*see* below).

Each fatty acid contains a long hydrophobic hydrocarbon chain (that is, one which is not soluble in water) and a terminal carboxylic acid group (COOH) which is extremely hydrophilic (i.e. water soluble). The chain lengths vary from one to nearly 30 carbon atoms and may be saturated or unsaturated. Saturated fats have all their available chemical bonds filled with hydrogen atoms and cannot join with other compounds. Unsaturated fats do not have the full complement of hydrogen atoms in their structure and have a softer or more liquid consistency.

Fatty acids have three major functions in the human body:

1 They are the building blocks of phospholipids (lipids containing phosphate) and glycolipids (lipids containing carbohydrate). These molecules are vital components of the outer, surrounding membranes of all cells, controlling the passage of substances both inwards and outwards.

2 Fatty acid derivatives, i.e. compounds that are made from them, serve as hormones and chemical messengers within and between cells.

3 Fatty acids are stored within cells as triglycerides (i.e. joined to a glycerol molecule) as fuel reserves. They are broken down when required to release large quantities of energy.

Saturated fats such as cholesterol are found in meat and dairy products, i.e. whole milk, cheese, butter and eggs. Many processed foods have saturated fats added to them and they are widely used in manufacturing. Saturated fatty acids are converted by liver cells into cholesterol which is an important substance in the body, being a component of cell membranes and a precursor in the production of steroid (sex) hormones and bile salts. However, an excess level in the blood causes atheroma or furring of the arteries which is a causal factor in angina, strokes and various forms of heart disease and is a feature of diabetes mellitus. Men are at particular risk of premature death from strokes and heart disease and it has been proved that a diet rich in saturated fat, and hence cholesterol, increases the risk of the development of these conditions. It is universally accepted that the diet of people in western countries contains an excess of saturated fat and every year many people suffer from the consequences of this. However, it is relatively simple to make adjustments to the diet and reduce consumption. Basic measures include:

1 Changing from full fat to semi-skimmed or skimmed milk

2 Grilling food instead of frying and cutting fat off meat before cooking

3 Using low fat, polyunsaturated vegetable oils and margarines

4 Choosing low fat cheeses and chicken or fish instead of meat

5 Eating less processed food, puddings, cakes, biscuits etc. which tend to have a high content of saturated fat

6 Eggs are an excellent food but are rich in cholesterol. Do not eat more than two or three each week

Unsaturated fats are of two types, polyunsaturated and monounsaturated. Polyunsaturated forms are found in vegetable oils, e.g. soya bean, sunflower, safflower and corn, soft margarines, nuts, seeds and oily fish. Among this group are the 'essential fatty acids' which are needed by the body for a number of vital functions and must be obtained from food. These include linolenic acid found in some plant oils, especially soya bean and ground nut oil. Linolenic acid forms about 20% of the total fatty acid content in triglycerides.

All the essential fatty acids are necessary constituents of cell membranes and are vital in the production of prostaglandins, which perform many functions in the body and are present in high levels in semen. Monounsaturated fats are found particularly in peanuts, olives (olive oil) and avocados, rape-seed and groundnut oil. Unlike saturated fats, consumption of unsaturated and polyunsaturated fats does not increase the level of blood cholesterol and there is good evidence to suggest that they have a beneficial, protective effect on the heart and circulation. Obviously, this is of importance to anyone who is at risk of developing heart disease. It is recommended that the consumption of all fat should be reduced so that it forms no more than 30% of the overall diet. The fat that is eaten should include more of the beneficial, unsaturated variety and it is helpful to eat oily fish, e.g. herring, mackerel, salmon, sardines, etc. about twice a week. Fish oils can be helpful for those suffering from a number of common disorders including eczema, psoriasis and arthritis as well as having beneficial effects on the circulatory system.

Fibre

Fibre is derived from plants and is found in fruit, vegetables, wholemeal flour and bread, bran-rich foods, brown rice, pasta and spaghetti, cereals including oats, beans and pulses. It is relatively indigestible and enhances the passage of food through the digestive system, helping to prevent constipation. The presence of fibre regulates the absorption of fats and glucose into the bloodstream. Oats have been shown to be particularly beneficial in lowering blood cholesterol levels. It has been shown that continual insufficient consumption of fibre has serious consequences for human health and is linked to the development of colorectal cancer (especially if the diet is also high in fat), some cases of irritable bowel syndrome, constipation and increased likelihood of high blood cholesterol levels.

Colorectal cancer (of the colon or rectum) is the third most common type of cancer among men, usually striking those in middle to older age (50 to 70 years). It is believed that if healthy people increase their daily fibre consumption to 25 grams or more each day, then this helps to prevent the development of this form of cancer. Once again, adjustments can be made quite easily by, for example, choosing wholemeal instead of white bread and high fibre breakfast cereals. In addition, it is recommended that at least five portions of vegetables and fruit should be eaten each day, which provide vitamins and minerals as well as fibre.

Vitamins and minerals

Vitamins are a group of organic substances that are required in minute quantities in the diet in order to maintain good health. A lack of a particular vitamin results in a deficiency disease. There are two groups of vitamins; those which are fat-soluble, including A, D, E and K and those which are water-soluble, C (ascorbic acid) and B (thiamine). The six vitamin groups are as follows:

1 A or retinol must be obtained from the diet and is needed for the manufacture of rhodopsin, a light-sensitive pigment, also called visual purple, which is essential for night vision. Vitamin A is also needed for the maintenance of skin and tissues and good sources are green vegetables, dairy products, liver and fish oils. A deficiency causes night blindness and possible total loss of vision.

2 B complex including thiamine, riboflavin, nicotinic acid, pantothenic acid, biotin, folic acid, B_6, pyroxidine, B_{12} (cyanocobalamin) and lipoic acid. These are required in the manufacture of red blood cells for maintenance of nerves and for enzyme activity and for amino acid metabolism. They must be obtained from the diet and sources include green vegetables, dairy products, cereals, grains, eggs, liver, meat, nuts, seeds, potatoes and fish. A deficiency in vitamin B causes beri beri while a lack of some of the others can result in anaemia and deterioration of the nervous system (B_{12}).

3 C (ascorbic acid) must be obtained on a daily basis from food because any excess is excreted and not stored. It is needed for maintenance of cell walls and connective tissue including blood vessels and tendons. It also helps the absorption of iron into the body, re-

leased during digestion. A deficiency causes fragility of skin, blood vessels and tendons characteristic of the disease known as scurvy.

4 D is a fat soluble vitamin occurring as two steroid derivatives: D_2 or calciferol in yeast and D_3 or cholecalciferol which can be produced by the skin, using cholesterol, in the presence of sunlight. It controls calcium levels in the blood, prompting increased uptake of the mineral from the digestion of food and hence making it available for bone growth and repair. Hence a deficiency of vitamin D causes bone deformities – rickets in children and osteomalacia in adults. Dietary sources are fish oils, eggs and dairy products.

5 E or tocopherol comprises several compounds that are essential for the maintenance of cell membranes. It is found in such foods as cereal grains, green vegetables and eggs but deficiency is rare as it is common in the diet.

6 K or phylloquinone, a compound form, acts as a coenzyme in protein synthesis in blood clotting. Green vegetables and egg yolks are good dietary sources but deficiency is rare as it is also manufactured by normal gut bacteria. If it does occur (i.e. if normal gut bacteria are, for any reason, disrupted or destroyed) the result may be severe bleeding.

Minerals are chemical elements which, like vitamins, are needed in minute quantities in the diet. Examples include calcium, zinc, iron, sodium and potassium and they are vital in many internal metabolic processes from the production of blood and bone to the transmission of nerve impulses. A deficiency can lead to the development of a particular condition and a good example of this is some forms of anaemia which can be caused or exacerbated by a lack of dietary iron. Minerals are found in many foods including green vegetables, fruits, cereals, grains, nuts, seeds, dairy products, meat, eggs and fish.

Water

Fluid intake in the form of water-based drinks, is essential for good health and is something which is easily overlooked. Many people are happy to consume tea, coffee, canned beverages and alcoholic drinks but water and fruit juice are sometimes less acceptable. Studies have shown that many people rarely drink plain water and young people can be particularly reluctant to do so. The recommendation is that at least 6 to 8 glasses of plain water should be drunk each day. Fruit juices or low sugar squashes, tea and coffee are useful alternatives, but the latter contain caffeine, which is not recommended in excess, and is unhelpful in some medical conditions. Carbonated soft drinks should be taken in moderation, particularly those which have a high sugar content. Water is essential for the correct functioning of the kidneys and bowels and more is needed in hot weather to compensate for the natural loss through sweating. It is a good idea to have several glasses of water after consuming alcohol, especially in the case of strong drinks such as neat spirits.

Salt

As well as being too high in fat, it is recognised that in general the western diet contains far too much salt. An excess intake of salt puts a strain on the kidneys and can contribute towards disease in these organs and also, the development of high blood pressure and heart disorders to which men are susceptible. A high salt intake is also likely to exacerbate existing disorders in these areas. Most processed foods have a high salt content and this can be true of otherwise 'healthy' items such as breakfast cereals and wholemeal bread. Also, a high salt content can be disguised in such items as sweet biscuits, sauces, baked beans, etc, where its presence is not always obvious. A small amount of salt is necessary for vital body processes but this is obtained naturally from a balanced, varied diet. Hence in order to reduce intake, no salt should be added to food, either during cooking or at the table. The consumption of processed foods should be limited and low-salt varieties chosen whenever possible. Many people enjoy the taste of salt, which enhances the flavour of food, and may find it difficult to reduce their intake. A number of salt substitutes are available, which are usually higher in potassium rather than sodium and these can be used sparingly as alternatives. Also, increasing the use of herbs and spices in cooking, if these are enjoyed, can help to make the lack of salt less noticeable. It is important to continue to enjoy food and for healthy people, it may be more realistic to aim for a reduction in salt intake rather than eliminating it altogether. Also, if a salty meal has been eaten, it is helpful to drink one or two extra glasses of water to aid the function of the kidneys.

Diet and shiatsu

It is important that allied with the routine of shiatsu, there should be a complementary planned diet and bearing in mind the information presented above, it is possible to recommend a routine to follow. As already implied, many advocate a minimum of animal proteins. In general, artificial foods such as sweeteners and refined foods (i.e. white sugar, flour, etc) are avoided and preference is given to consumption of vegetables and fruit. Whole grains are considered very important and the following list provides some indication of the types of food that are ideal.

grains	–	whole wheat, brown rice, oats, corn, barley, maize, millet.
all fruits	–	apples, pears, berries and so on.
nuts	–	cashews (unsalted), almonds, walnuts.
vegetables	–	(just about any) broccoli, cauliflower, cabbage, carrots, leeks, onions, green beans, sprouts, kale, spinach, salad greens, bean sprouts, etc.
pulses	–	all lentils, aduki beans, red kidney beans, chick peas, soya beans, mung beans and split peas.
fish	–	most varieties.

There are additional items which will vary between countries and regions, for example seaweed is used in many places. This provides a good source of iodine, B vitamins and numerous minerals.

A note on the macrobiotic diet

The macrobiotic (meaning *large* and *life*) diet essentially began with a Japanese doctor in the late 19th century. The diet was based on whole grain cereals and vegetables and it was later developed further as giving greater resistance to disease and providing more energy. The diet, just as in everything else, depended upon a balance of yin and yang (as described above). The diet is high in fibre and can help reduce weight problems, cholesterol levels, constipation and so on, but it absolutely vital that it is combined with other foods to give the balanced supply of vitamins which an extreme macrobiotic diet lacks. Thus in shiatsu, there is the inclusion of many other foods, especially vegetables and fruit and a sensible macrobiotic diet will now contain whole grain cereals, fruit, vegetables (including seaweed), soups (pulses, soya, etc), and seeds and nuts. This ensures that dietary components such as vitamin D and B_{12} are included.

Energy or Ki

As mentioned earlier ki, or qi (*see* figure 2), manifested as yin and yang, is the vital force or energy of life. A balance is vital and it is also accepted that ki, through yin and yang is the basis of the five elements: water, wood, fire, earth and metal which then constitute the entire universe. In addition, the five elements represent our bodily make-up. The ki flows into us and through by means of channels called meridians (*see* page 43) and each meridian is linked to one of the five elements. The meridians contain pressure points which are the focus of attention in shiatsu, because blockages here have to be released to restore balance.

Figure 2 – the symbol for ki

Auras

There are believed to be a number of auras, or energy layers, that surround the physical body and can be detected or appreciated (*see* figure 3). The first layer, the etheric body, is the most dense and is connected with the body and the way it works. An exercise is described later that enables this layer to be detected (*see* page 47). The astral body is much wider, is affected by people's feelings and, if viewed by a clairvoyant, is said to change in colour and shape depending on the feelings being experienced. The next aura is the mental body, which is involved with the thought processes and intelligence of a person. Similarly, this can be viewed by a clairvoyant and is said to contain 'pictures' of ideas emanating from the person. These first three auras comprise the personality of a person. The last aura is known as the causal body, soul or higher self. This is concerned more with perceptive feelings and comprehension. It is believed in reincarnation that the first three auras die with the body, but the causal body carries on in its process of development by adopting another personality. As a person grows in maturity and awareness, these different auras are used, and energy is passed from one layer to another. It therefore follows that any alteration in the physical state will, in turn, affect the other layers, and vice versa.

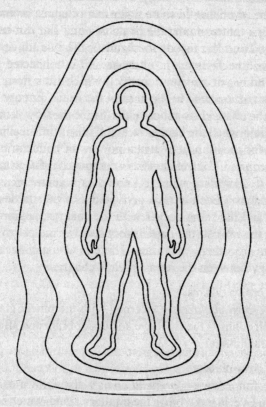

Figure 3 – auras

Seven centres of energy, or chakras

It is believed that there are seven main chakras (a chakra being a centre of energy) found in a mid-line down the body, from the top of the head to the bottom of the torso (*see* figure 4). They are situated along the sushumna, or spiritual channel, which runs from the crown of the head to the base of the trunk. Energy enters the channel from both ends. Since the flow is most efficient when the back is straight, this is the ideal posture for meditation or when powers of concentration are required. Each chakra has a component of each aura, and it comprises what is known as a centre of consciousness. Each aura is activated as a person develops, and the same occurs with the chakras, beginning with the lowest (the base or root chakra) and progressing to the others with time. There is also a change of energy between the auras of each chakra.

The crown chakra

The *crown chakra* is concerned with the pineal gland, which controls the right eye and upper brain and affects spiritual matters.

The brow chakra

The *ajna, brow* or *forehead chakra* also known as the Third Eye, is linked with the pituitary gland, which controls the left eye, lower brain, nose and nervous system.

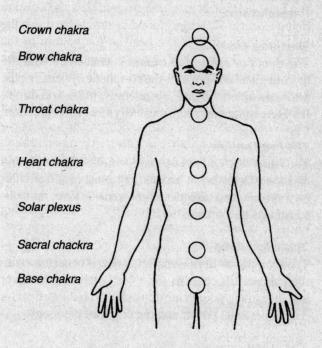

Crown chakra

Brow chakra

Throat chakra

Heart chakra

Solar plexus

Sacral chackra

Base chakra

Figure 4 – the major chakras

It has an effect on the intellect, perception, intuition and comprehension.

The throat chakra

The *throat* or *expressive chakra* is concerned with the thyroid gland and governs the lymphatic system, hands, arms, shoulders, mouth, vocal cords, lungs and throat. It affects communication, creativity and self-expression.

The heart chakra

The *heart chakra* is concerned with the thymus gland and controls the heart, breasts, vagus nerve and circulatory system, and affects self-awareness, love, humanitarian acts and compassion.

The solar plexus

The *solar plexus* or *personality chakra* is concerned with the pancreas. It controls the spleen, gall bladder, liver and digestive system and stomach, and has an effect on desire, personal power and the origin of emotions.

The sacral chakra

The *sacral* or *sexual chakra* affects the gonads and controls the lower back, feet, legs and reproductive system. This affects physical, sexual and mental energy, relationships and self-worth.

The base chakra

The *base* or *root chakra* is concerned with the adrenal glands. It controls the skeleton, parasympathetic and sympathetic nervous systems, bladder and kidneys, and affects reproduction and the physical will. As an example of this, if a person is suffering from an ailment of the throat, it is possible that he or she may also be unable to voice private thoughts and feelings.

Zang and fu organs – energy storage and production

According to traditional Eastern therapies, organs have a dual function—their physical one and another that is concerned with the use of energy and might be termed an 'energetic function'. The twelve organs mentioned in the traditional therapies are split into two groups known as zang and fu, and each is described below.

Zang organs are for energy storage, and the fu organs produce energy from sustenance and drink and also control excretion. The organs can be listed in pairs, each zang matched by a fu with a similar function. Although the pancreas is not specifically mentioned, it is usually included with the spleen. The same applies to the 'triple heater' or 'triple burner', which is connected with the solar plexus, lower abdomen and the thorax. The lungs are a zang organ and are concerned with assimilation of

energy, or ki, from the air, which with energy from food
ensures the complete body is fed and that mental alertness and a positive attitude are maintained. This is paired
with the fu organ of the large intestine, which takes sustenance from the small intestine, absorbs necessary liq-
uids and excretes waste material via the faeces. It is also
concerned with self-confidence. The spleen is a zang
organ and changes energy or ki from food into energy
that is needed by the body. It is concerned with the mental functions of concentration, thinking and analysing.
This is paired with the fu organ of the stomach, which
prepares food so that nutrients can be extracted and also
any energy, or ki, can be taken. It also provides 'food
for thought'. The zang organ of the heart assists blood
formation from ki and controls the flow of blood and
the blood vessels. It is where the mind is housed and
therefore affects awareness, belief, long-term memory
and feelings. This is paired with the fu organ of the small
intestine, which divides food into necessary and unnec-
essary parts, the latter passing to the large intestine. It is
also concerned with the making of decisions. The kidneys are a zang organ and they produce basic energy, or
ki, for the other five paired organs and also for reproduction, birth, development and maturity. They also sus-
tain the skeleton and brain and provide willpower and
'get up and go'. They are paired with the fu organ of the

bladder, which stores waste fluids until they are passed as urine and also gives strength or courage. The zang organ of the 'heart governor' is concerned with the flow of blood throughout the body. It is a protector and help for the heart and has a bearing on relationships with other people (although there is no organ known as the 'heart governor' it is connected with the heart and its functions). This is paired with the 'triple heater' or 'burner', which passes ki around the body and allows an emotional exchange with others. The liver is the sixth zang organ, and it assists with a regular flow of ki to achieve the most favourable physiological effects and emotional calmness. Positive feelings, humour, planning and creativity are also connected with it. The gall bladder is the sixth fu organ, with which the liver is paired, and this keeps bile from the liver and passes it to the intestines. It concerns decision-making and forward thinking.

The meridian system

The meridians, as previously mentioned, are a system of invisible channels on the back and front of the body along which energy, or ki, flows. There are twelve principal meridians plus two additional ones, which are called the governing vessel and the conception or directing vessel. Each meridian passes partly through the body and partly along the skin, joining various chakras

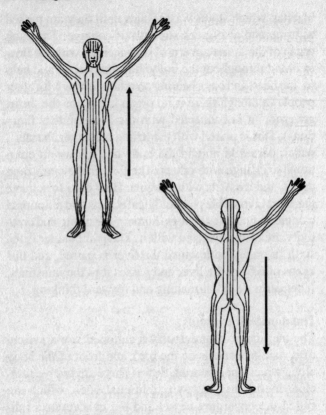

Figure 5 – the meridian system

and organs (the organs as recognised in traditional Eastern medicine). One end of every meridian is beneath the skin while the other is on the surface of the skin on the feet or hands. Along each meridian are acupressure or acupuncture points, which in shiatsu are called tsubos. These points allow the flow of energy along the meridian to be altered if necessary (*see* figure 5). The meridians receive energy from the chakras and organs (as described previously), from the meridians with ends located on the feet and hands and also via the pressure points, or tsubos. Energy, or ki, can pass from one meridian into another as there is a 'pathway' linking each meridian to two others. The energy passes in a continuous cycle or flow and in a set order from one meridian to another. By working on the meridians, and particularly the pressure points, a number of beneficial effects can be achieved with problems such as muscle tension, backache and headache. Since the flow of energy is stimulated by working on the meridians this will in turn affect the joints, muscles and skin and thereby ease these complaints. Since a person's mental state, feelings and moods are also altered by the flow of energy, this can induce a more positive frame of mind.

A person in good health should have a constant flow of ki, with no concentrations or imbalances in any part of the body. It is believed that the greater the amount of ki there is within a person's body, the greater the vitality, mental alertness and overall awareness that person will possess.

Feeling ki

It is possible for a person to 'feel' ki, and the following exercise helps demonstrate what it is like. Stand upright with the feet apart and the arms stretched upwards. Rub the hands together as if they were very cold, so that a feeling of warmth is generated. The backs of the hands, wrists and forearms should also be rubbed. The arms should be put down at the side of the body and shaken vigorously. This should then be repeated from the beginning, with the arms above the head and concluding with the shaking. Then hold the hands out to the front – they should have a pleasant feeling of warmth and vitality, which is due to the circulation of blood and energy that has been generated. The hands should be placed to the sides, then after inhaling deeply concentrate on relaxing as you exhale. This procedure should be done several times, and then it should be possible to feel the ki. The hands should be placed about 1 m (3 feet) apart, with the palms of the hands facing inwards. After relaxation, concentrate your thoughts on the gap between your hands and then gradually reduce the space between them – but they must not touch. It is likely that when the hands come quite close, about 15–30 cm (6–12 inches), a feeling of tingling or warmth may be felt, or the sensation that there is something between the hands. This will be when the auras that surround the hands touch. To reinforce the sensation, the hands should be taken apart again and then closed together so that the feeling is experienced again and becomes more familiar.

The following exercise also enables ki to be felt, but this time it is the etheric aura around another person's head and shoulders. The previous procedure to generate

Figure 6 – feeling ki

ki should be repeated, but this time the hand should be placed near to another person's head, within 60 cm–1 m (2–3 feet). This person should be sitting upright on the floor or on a chair. The hand should be moved gradually nearer to the seated person's head, concentrating attention on the gap between your hand and his or her head (*see* figure 6). If no sensation is felt, the hand should be moved back to its original position and the process should be repeated. Again, a feeling of tingling or warmth will probably be experienced as the person's aura is felt. When this has been achieved, the hand can progress round the head and down to the shoulders, noting the edge of the aura at the same time. If the person has no success in experiencing the aura, it is likely that the mind is not clear of other thoughts, so relaxation is suggested prior to any further attempt.

It is also possible for a person, by concentrating his or her thoughts and by a slight change of position, to alter the flow of ki in the body. This will have the effect of either making him or her feel a lot heavier or lighter, depending on which is desired. Taken to extremes, someone who is skilled at the control of ki will prove too heavy to be lifted by four people.

Basic Rules

There are some basic rules that should be followed before the practice of shiatsu. Clothing should be comfortable, loose-fitting and made of natural fibres since this will help with the flow of energy or ki. The room should be warm, quiet, have adequate space and be neat and clean. If not, this can have an adverse effect on the flow of ki. The person receiving the therapy should ideally lie on a futon (a quilted Japanese mattress) or similar mat on the floor. If necessary, pillows or cushions should be ready to hand if the person does not feel comfortable. Shiatsu should not be given or received by someone who has just eaten a large meal—it is advisable to delay for several hours. No pressure should be exerted on varicose veins or injuries such as cuts or breaks in bones. Although shiatsu can be of benefit to women while pregnant, there are four areas that should be avoided and these are the stomach, any part of the legs from the knees downwards, the fleshy web of skin between the forefinger and thumb, and an area on the shoulders at each side of the neck. Ensure that the person is calm and relaxed. It is generally not advisable to practise shiatsu on people who have serious illnesses such as heart disorders, multiple sclerosis or cancer. An experienced practitioner may be able to help, but a detailed and accurate diagnosis and course of treatment is essential. A verbal check on the person's overall health is important and also to ascertain if a woman is pregnant. If there is any worry or doubt about proceeding, then the safest option is not to go ahead.

It often helps to prepare for a treatment through a short period of meditation or breathing exercises and of course the person giving the shiatsu should have clean hands, well manicured, to make the treatment comfortable. The recipient may shower before the treatment – this will help promote the circulation and overall relaxation. The person giving the treatment should be aware of their body position, and it is always necessary to adopt a comfortable and easily maintained stance. Bending over the recipient should be done properly to avoid straining the back. The pattern of breathing is very important – it should be rhythmic and deep and if it can be synchronised to that of the recipient, then it will enhance the treatment.

Although the general feeling after receiving shiatsu is one of well-being and relaxation, there are occasionally unpleasant results, such as coughing, generation of mucus or symptoms of a cold; a feeling of tiredness; a headache or other pains and aches; or feeling emotional (*see also* Side Effects?). The coughing and production of mucus is due to the body being encouraged to rid itself of its surplus foods (such as sugars and fats) in this form. A cold can sometimes develop when the mucus is produced, usually when the cells of the body are not healthy. Tiredness can occur, frequently with a person who suffers from nervous tension. After therapy has removed this stress or tension, then the body's need for sleep and rest becomes apparent. A short-lived headache or other pain may also develop, for which there are two main reasons. Since shiatsu redresses the balance of ki in the body, this means that blockages in the flow of energy are released and the ki can rush around the body, causing a temporary imbalance in one part and resulting in an ache or pain. It is also possible that too much time or pressure may have been applied to a particular area. The amount needed varies considerably from one person to another. If a pain or headache is still present after a few days, however, it is sensible to obtain qualified medical help. Emotional feelings can occur while the energy is being stimulated to flow and balance is regained. The feelings may be connected with something from the past that has been suppressed and so, when these emotions resurface, it is best for them to be expressed in a way that is beneficial, such as crying. There may, of course, be no reaction at all. Some people are completely 'out of touch' with their bodies and are aware only that all is not well when pain is felt. If this is so, then any beneficial effects from shiatsu may not register. Because of a modern diet that contains an abundance of animal fats, people become overweight through the deposition of fat below the skin and around the internal organs. The body is unable to 'burn off' this fat, and this layer forms a barrier to ki. The flow is stopped, and overweight people do not tend to benefit as much because of the difficulty in stimulating the flow of ki in the body.

Exercises and the three main centres

The body is divided into three main centres – the head, the heart, and the abdominal centres. The head centre is concerned with activities of a mental nature, such as imaginative and intellectual thought processes, and is concerned with the brow chakra. The heart centre is concerned with interactions among people and to the world in general, including the natural world. It is related to the chakra of the throat and heart. The abdominal centre is related to the base, sacral and solar plexus chakras and is concerned with the practical aspects of life and physical activity. Ideally, energy should be divided equally among the three but because of a number of factors, such as activity, education, diet, culture, etc, this is frequently not so. In shiatsu, more importance is attached to the abdominal centre, known as the hara. The following exercise uses abdominal breathing and, by so doing, not only is oxygen inhaled but also ki is taken into the hara where it increases a person's vitality. Once the technique is mastered, it can be practised virtually anywhere and will restore composure and calmness.

Sit on the floor with the back straight and, if possible, in the position known in Japan as seiza (*see* figure 7).

Figure 7 – seiza

Practising Shiatsu

The hands should be placed loosely together in the lap and the mind and body should become relaxed after some deep breathing. One hand should be put on the stomach, below the navel, and the other on the chest. When inhaling, this should not be done with the chest but with the abdomen, which should increase in size. As the person exhales the abdomen should contract, and this procedure should be practised for a few minutes. After a rest it should be repeated, inhaling quite deeply but still the chest should not be allowed to rise. Some people may not find this exercise at all difficult while others may need more practice. It may be that there is stress or tension in the diaphragm. Once the technique has been mastered and the hands do not need to be placed on the chest and abdomen, imagine that ki is being inhaled down into the hara. Sit in the same position and inhale slowly via the nose and imagine the ki descending (*see* figure 8). (It may aid concentration if the eyes are closed.) The breath should be held for about four seconds and concentration should be centred on the ki. Then exhale gradually through the mouth and repeat the process for a few minutes.

The next exercise is known as a centred movement, which practises movement of the ki, since it is one person's ki that should have an effect on another. After practising shiatsu on a partner, you should not feel tired but

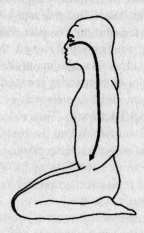

Figure 8 – inhaling through the nose

refreshed and exhilarated. This is a benefit of the extra ki in the body. The exercise should be begun on hands and knees (a body width apart), and it is most important that you are relaxed and comfortable with no tension. This position is the basis for other movements that are practised on others. While the position is maintained, begin to move the body backwards and forwards so that you are conscious of the transfer of weight, either on to the hands or knees. The body should then be moved slowly in a circular way, again being aware of the shift of weight from the hands, to hands and knees, to knees, etc, returning to the original position. You should also realise that as the whole body is moved, the abdomen is its 'centre of gravity'. Practise maintaining a position for about five seconds, registering the increase in weight on the hands when you move forwards and the reduction when you rock backwards. Then return to the original position. It is important that the body weight is always used at right angles to the receiver as this will have the maximum effect on the flow of ki. The reason for holding a particular position is that this has the effect of making the person's ki move.

The centred movement previously described can be practised on a partner in exactly the same way, following the same rules. The right hand should be placed on the sacrum, which is between the hips, and the left hand midway between the shoulder blades. As before, you should rock forwards and hold the position for about five seconds and then repeat after rocking backwards on to the knees (*see* figure 9). This basic procedure can be repeated about twelve times, and if you are not sure whether too much or too little pressure is being used, check with your partner. You will eventually acquire the skill of knowing what amount is right for a particular person.

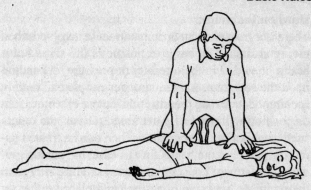

Figure 9 – a centred movement

To summarise, there are some basic rules to be followed when practising shiatsu. A person should make use of body weight and not muscular strength, and there should be no effort involved. At all times a calm and relaxed state should be maintained, and the weight of the body should be at right angles in relation to the receiver's body. The person's whole body should be moved when altering weight on to the receiver, maintaining the hara as the centre. Any weight or pressure held should be for a short time only and both hands should be used equally. It is best to maintain a regular pattern of movement while giving shiatsu, and always keep in physical contact with the receiver by keeping a hand on him or her throughout the therapy.

More on technique

There is a great element of common sense involved when giving shiatsu. The basic technique is the same but it has to be varied in the intensity or pressure, depending upon the recipient. Larger, stronger people can readily accommodate strong pressure while those of a more frail disposition will need a lighter touch. These, and others such as children or pregnant women can be treated using the palms of the hands. In this case, the person giving the treatment concentrates upon sending energy to the recipient, focusing upon the hand placed either on or just above the body.

In summary:
- for a large, strong recipient – apply reasonable weight and pressure
- a person with plenty of energy – use shiatsu to calm and relax
- a person with little energy – firm shiatsu to rebuild and reinforce
- a healthy child – standard shiatsu but with reduced pressure and possibly overall a shorter programme
- an elderly person – proceed very gently with much reduced pressure, little stretching
- the pressure and rigour of the routine can be varied for healthy individuals, depending upon the individu-

al's pain threshold. This does not mean that the pressure should create pain – exactly the opposite – but each person differs in the amount and duration of the pressure with which they feel comfortable.

Quite often, the treatment will consist of a relaxation session followed by attention to the whole body or specific areas. The relaxation is best done with the recipient laying down. Pressure is applied to the upper back, on either side of the spine (*see* figure 10) and the pressure is moved up and down the spine. This helps relax the whole body.

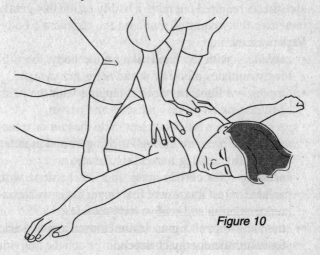

Figure 10

In treating the whole body, the head, neck, shoulders and back, arms, abdomen and legs should be dealt with. If necessary, a particular part of the problem with which there is a problem, can be dealt with, especially if there is not sufficient time to treat the whole body. The pressure used in the application of shiatsu helps the circulation (of both blood and lymph) and also increases flexibility in joints. By also assisting proper nervous function, the body's resistance to disease is enhanced.

A number of variations of touch can be used to apply the pressure necessary. However, it is not just crude pressure that is required but more a bodily action that gently increases the weight of touch on the recipient's body. Variations include:

- *rubbing* – with the hands flat on the body, the rubbing stimulates blood flow and helps muscle tone.
- *tapping* – a light, rhythmical tapping with the palm or fingers helps vitalise muscles and nerves.
- *pressing* – the whole body leans into the motion transmitting the pressure through the fingers and thumbs, or the palm creating muscular relaxation.
- *kneading* – for certain areas, this can be done with the hand or just thumb and first finger to gently stimulate circulation and relieve hard muscles.
- *stretching* – to relax muscles and loosen joints, it also stimulates the energy channels.

It is always helpful if both parties can co-ordinate their breathing and it can be timed at a particular and appropriate point in the routine.

Side Effects?

In most cases, shiatsu leaves the recipient feeling much more relaxed, flexible and lithe. In addition, it often results in the individual sleeping better, and because of the release of knotted, tense areas, and probably also minor aches and pains, their general demeanour is much improved and mentally they feel much more lively.

However, in common with many other practices of a similar nature where the body has to be cleared of toxins, blockages or imbalances, the first few sessions of shiatsu may produce effects which are not expected in that they are more unpleasant than pleasant. They are generally very minor complaints due to the body readjusting to a more correct and balanced state through the elimination of fluid. These are some reactions that may occur, albeit temporarily:

Aches and pains

Headaches or other bodily pains may occur but are usually short-lived. The ache may be due simply to a particular area of the body receiving too much attention and so it is important to apply the correct pressure for the appropriate time. Guidelines are given elsewhere on how to gauge treatment duration. Clearly, if someone is susceptible to headaches or even migraine then particular care must be taken and it would then be appropriate to concentrate upon the neck and shoulders and the rest of the body to help restore the balance of ki. The headaches may in any case be due to an excess of ki, so working on the head would not be beneficial. Clearing blockages elsewhere will help replace the balance and thereby help the head. A continuing headache should obviously be referred to an appropriate medical practitioner.

Such aches may also be caused by the sudden release of ki which has been blocked. When it is released there may be a deficiency elsewhere in the body causing a passing pain. In this case, the recipient can be reassured that this is a temporary phenomenon and will clear shortly.

Symptoms of colds

It is not uncommon for someone receiving shiatsu to develop symptoms ordinarily associated with a cold. This may be seen as a runny nose or a cough. This is merely the body reacting to the treatment and producing mucus to enable it to get rid of the excesses which are upsetting the balance. This may develop into a cold proper with the associated symptoms of lethargy, aching limbs and so on, but this is not a cause for concern. It will gradually disappear and with it the general well being will improve.

Tiredness

Some feeling of tiredness is likely to be felt by most people after shiatsu. This is not at all unexpected as the treatment induces relaxation and this often encourages sleep! Some individuals, however, may feel totally washed out but this can be remedied by a complete rest. This state is simply a response of the body to the lifting of tension and stress by the shiatsu treatment.

Other responses

It is perhaps a less common effect, but release of tension may be accompanied by an emotional release. This can be left to run its natural course, with gentle comfort from the person giving the treatment. An equally common feeling may be that nothing is experienced. This is not altogether unexpected because the style of modern living is such that there can be many barriers to feeling the effects of the ki and it may take a little time before the individual becomes attuned to the flow of ki and the beneficial effects of shiatsu.

Applying Shiatsu

Shiatsu on the face and head

There are a large number of different exercises and techniques, but at each time the giver must be relaxed and calm to enable the flow of ki to occur and thus make the shiatsu work to full effect. As an example, the following exercise on the face and head begins with the receiver's head being held firmly in one hand and, using the thumb of the other hand, pressing upwards in a straight line between the eyebrows towards the hairline. Each movement should only be quite small, about 12 millimetres (0.5 inch). The fingers should then be placed on each side of the head and both thumbs used to press from the inner end of the eyebrows towards the hairline (*see* figure 11a). Again, holding the hands at each side of the head, the thumbs should then be used to press from the start of the eyebrows across the brow to the outside (11b). With the fingers in place at each side of the face, work the thumbs across the bone below the eyes, moving approximately 6 millimetres (0.25 inch) at a time (11c). Commencing with the thumbs a little to

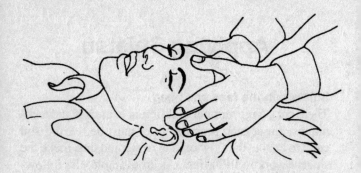

Figure 11 a – press between the eyebrows towards the hairline

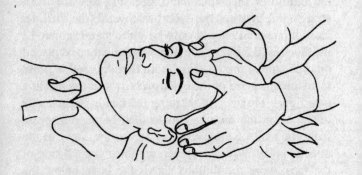

Figure 11 b – press from the eyebrows across the brow

Figure 11 c – work the thumbs across the bone below the eyes

Figure 11 d – press across the face below the cheekbones

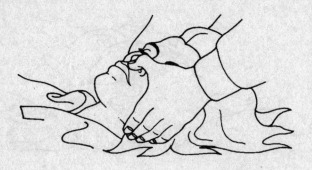

Figure 11 e – press the area between the nose and upper lip

Figure 11 f – press with the thumbs outwards over the upper jaw

Figure 11 g – press outwards over the lower part of the jaw

Figure 11 h – place fingers beneath the jaw and lean back

one side of each nostril, press across the face below the cheekbones (11d). Press one thumb in the area between the top lip and nose (11e) and then press with both the thumbs outwards over the upper jaw (11f). Next, press one thumb in the hollow below the lower lip and then press outwards with both thumbs over the lower part of the jaw (11g). The giver then puts all fingers of the hands beneath the lower jaw and then leans backwards so that pressure is exerted (11h).

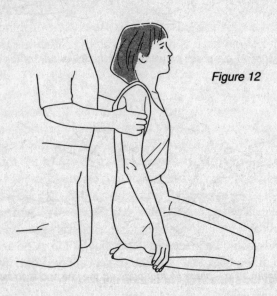

Figure 12

The neck and shoulders

As a preliminary to other moves a general loosening can be achieved by holding the arms a little below the shoulders and then lifting up and down. The recipient should be seated either on a chair or on the floor (figure 12). Next the shoulders can be kneaded, with the thumbs on to the back and the fingers over the front on to the collar bone. In this way, the muscles across the top of the back can be worked upon, inducing relaxation in that area. Rotation of the head is useful for releasing tension and the hands should be placed as shown in figure 13. The head is then rotated two or three times in each direction.

The back

There are many positions and variations that can be used, but below a few are mentioned. Start by kneeling to one side of the recipient, with the right hand at the base of the back and the left hand at the top between the shoulder blades. Then work with gentle pressure through the palm down to the side of the body and down to the waist, and then repeat for the other side (figure 14). Then position the hands as shown in figure 10. The base of each hand should be placed to either side of the spine at the top of the back and with the fingers splayed out, away from the spine. Weight is then applied, by leaning onto

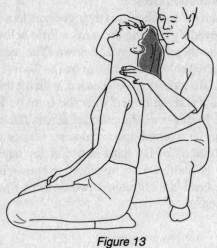

Figure 13

the recipient, and the hands are moved down the back, breathing out for each application of pressure and not forgetting to coordinate breathing whenever possible. Then with one hand palm down on the centre of the back, the second palm is placed on top and pressure applied. The prone position of the recipient is also a good position for kneading the shoulders and neck area, as shown in figure 15.

Next, place the hands on the back, thumbs to the cen-

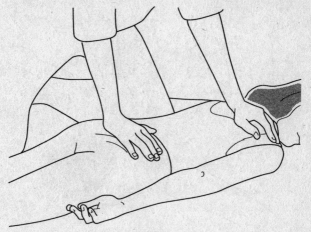

Figure 14

tre and fingers splayed away to the sides of the body. Put the thumbs just below the shoulder blades (*see* figure 16) about 4 centimetres away from the spine and on breathing out, press down and hold for 5 seconds. Then move down the spine to a position roughly alongside the next vertebra and continue in this fashion down the back to the base of the spine.

A number of positions are helpful for the shoulder, and increase flexibility. Figure 17 shows the arm bent around the back, while laying face down. It is important

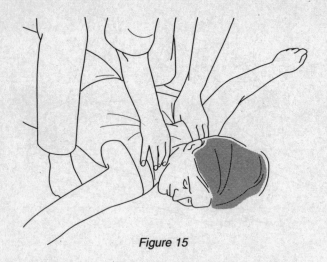

Figure 15

only to move the arm up the back as far as it will go, with comfort. It should not, obviously, be forced. Next, take the left arm by the wrist and with your right hand on the recipient's left shoulder, raise the left arm and stretch it a little (*see* figure 18). The arm should also be rotated in both directions a few times. These last two treatments can be performed on both arms.

Before turning our attention to the legs, it is worthwhile applying a movement to the buttocks. As in figure 19, place the left hand at the base of the spine and

74

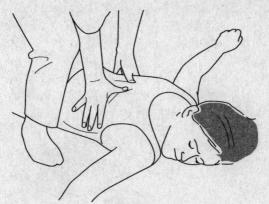

Figure 16

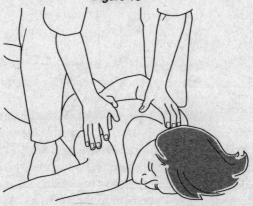

Figure 17

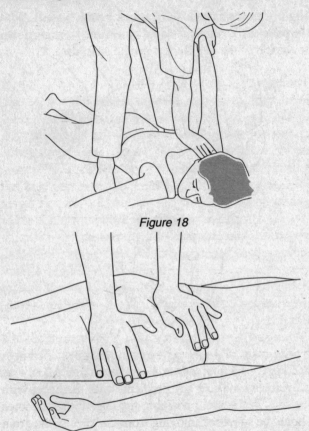

Figure 18

Figure 19

slightly to one side (to the buttock being treated). With the palm of the right hand apply pressure, working down to the top of the leg. Repeat on the other side.

The legs

While still laying face down, attention can now be paid to the legs. The position shown in figure 20 is an exercise to stretch the Achilles tendon. The leg is bent up at the knee and the foot held roughly horizontal and the toes are then bent down towards the floor. Then both legs are bent back at the knee and the feet are held and gently pushed on to the buttocks (as shown in figure 21). Now kneel next to the recipient and place either your left hand (or right hand, depending upon which side you are kneeling) at the base of the spine and with your other hand move progressively down the leg applying pressure with the palm (figure 22). A reasonable pressure can be applied providing the recipient is comfortable.

Lying on the back and with the legs outstretched and a little apart, place the palms of the hands on the knees and apply pressure, forwards and back (figure 23). This movement will help any problems with the knee. With the legs in the same position, the legs above the knee should be squeezed, moving from the knee to the groin and back. This helps muscle tone and circulation and

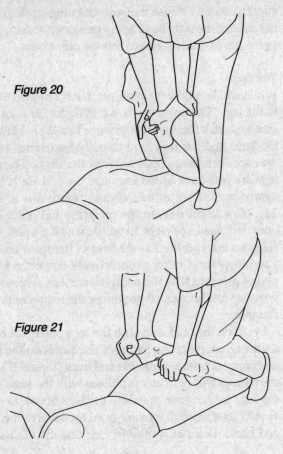

Figure 20

Figure 21

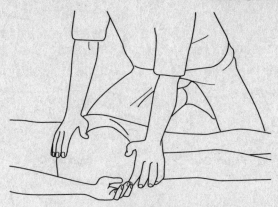

Figure 22

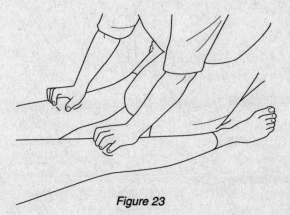

Figure 23

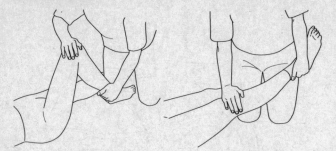

Figure 24a   *Figure 24b*

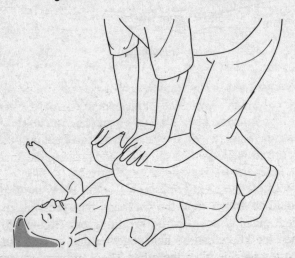

Figure 25

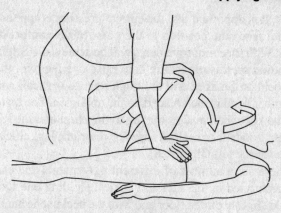

Figure 26

thereby assists in the circulation of energy around the body. Another movement that is good for joint flexibility is to hold the knee and ankle, pushing the ankle in towards the body and the knee upwards. Then pull the leg out straight, holding the ankle and pushing the knee flat when the leg is straight out (figure 24).

With the recipient lying on his or her back, the legs should be drawn up to the chest and then pressure applied, pushing down while breathing out (figure 25). Then the knees can be held together and pushed out, first to one side, then the other. These movements are good for the hips and lower back. As with all these positions, it is important that the correct pressure is applied; do not force the position to the point of discomfort or pain. With time, improvements will be achieved. A slight variation on this procedure is to raise one leg with the leg bent at the knee and the thigh near to vertical, and the other hand is then placed on the abdomen. The hand on the knee then pushes the leg to the chest and the leg is also rotated, anti-clockwise for the right leg, clockwise for the left (figure 26).

There are a number of different movements that can be performed on the feet and ankles. Holding one foot raised slightly off the floor and with the heel in one hand, push the toes first back and then forwards (figure 27). At the same time, while in this position, the foot can be rotated to work the ankle and promote flexibility.

The foot is worthy of some attention as it is commonly a source of problems. In addition, there are several therapies in which it figures prominently, notably reflexology. Developing this theme further, work each toe by applying pressure and gently rotating. Also, hold the foot with one hand and then work on each toe by holding the base of the toe, rotating the toe to flex the joint and then gently pull it away from the foot (figure 28). Pressure can also be applied to the sole of the foot and the sole can be drummed as this helps stimulate a number of body organs.

Figure 27a

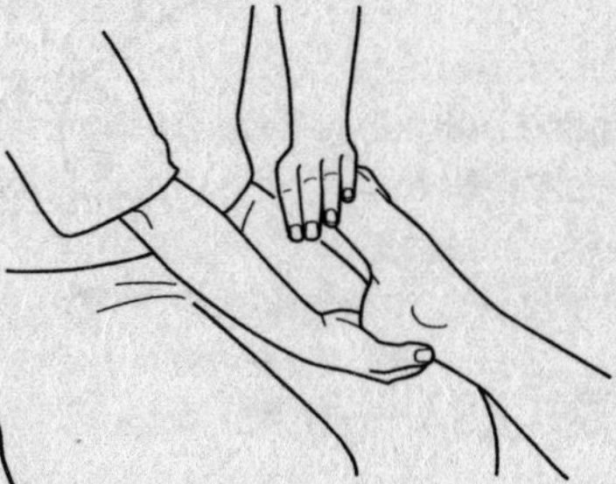

Figure 27b

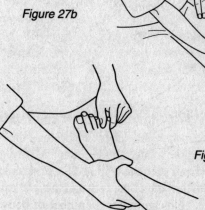

Figure 28

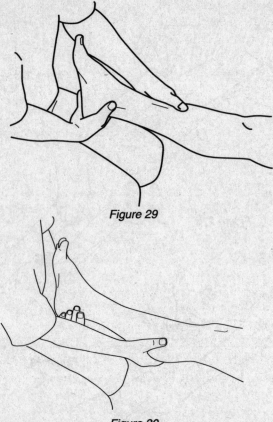

Figure 29

Figure 30

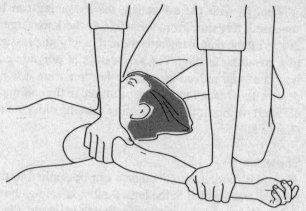

Figure 31

Figure 32

Then, as with the upper leg, the lower leg can be squeezed, this time from the ankle to the knee (figure 29). With the thumb towards the calf, applying pressure in a kneading fashion. The application of pressure can be varied and moved around the leg to ensure it is all dealt with. Then attention can be turned to the calf muscle itself, using similar squeezing/kneading movements (figure 30).

The arms

A similar routine of movements can be applied to the arms as was applied to the legs. Firstly, kneeling above the head, lay one arm out, palm facing upwards. Place one hand on the shoulder and with the other hand apply pressure with the palm along the length of the arm (figure 31). Then stretch the arm by holding the hand and wrist and pulling the arm above the head. This is good for the joints of the arm and shoulder (figure 32).

Holding the recipient's hand and starting at the shoulder, massage the upper arm pausing to apply pressure for a few seconds before moving down and finishing at the elbow (figure 33). This procedure can be repeated on the underarm with a gentle kneading movement (figure 34). The elbow joint can then be manipulated by bending the arm up at the elbow, flexing and rotating gently.

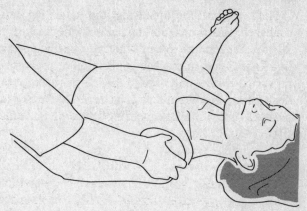

Figure 33

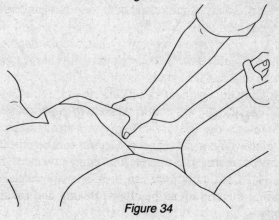

Figure 34

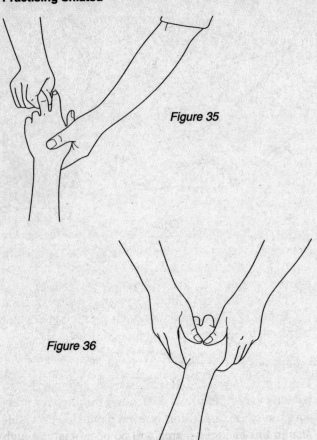

Figure 35

Figure 36

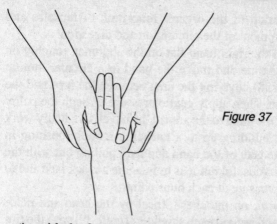

Figure 37

As with the feet and toes, so the hand and fingers are important for their effect on the body organs. Work individual fingers by squeezing along their length (figure 35) and then rub the back of the hand, working from the wrist and moving along each finger, applying pressure through the thumb (figure 36). On the palm of the hand, press with both thumbs in a circular motion (figure 37).

The body

Working on the area of the stomach and abdomen has to be done very carefully as sometimes the slightest pressure can cause discomfort or even pain. However, shiatsu in this abdominal area will be beneficial, through stimulation of the organs, relaxation of muscles and improvement of the circulation and digestion.

Place the right hand flat on the abdomen roughly on the waistline and move the hand in a circular motion (figure 38) covering the area between the hips and the rib cage. Then apply gentle pressure through the palm/heel of the hand to the area of the navel. Gradually work at this, building up to a kneading motion, pushing in with the heel of the hand and then pulling out with the fingers. A useful guide is to imagine a clock face and to apply pressure at each hour point.

To work on the chest, kneel by the head and place each hand around each shoulder (figure 39) with the fingers going down over the upper arm. The heel of each hand therefore rests naturally in the small hollow just inside the shoulder. Next lean on to the shoulders using your weight to apply the pressure. This should be held for just a few seconds and then relaxed, then repeated. This pushed the shoulders down towards the floor and the chest flexes and opens.

This series of movements approximates to a complete body treatment and if time permits it is useful to perform this sequence in each session of shiatsu. However, it is unlikely that time will always be available and in that case the areas requiring attention should be dealt with preferentially.

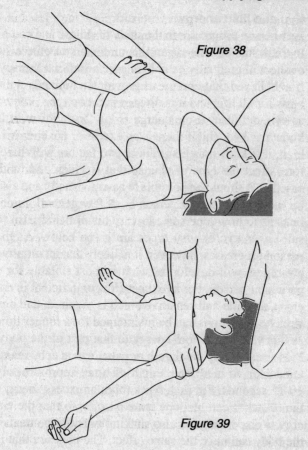

Figure 38

Figure 39

Kyo and jitsu energy

As a person progresses in the study of shiatsu and comes
to understand the needs and requirements of others, he
or she will gradually be able to give beneficial therapy.
It is believed that energy, as previously defined, is the
basis for all life, and it is divided into two types known
as kyo and jitsu. If the energy is low or deficient, it is
known as kyo, and if there is an excess or the energy is
high, it is known as jitsu. These two factors will therefore affect the type of shiatsu that is given and, with
practice, it should be possible to assess visually and also
by touch what type a person is. A few general guidelines as to how a person can vary his or her shiatsu to
suit either kyo or jitsu types are given below. As the
person progresses, however, it is likely that an intuitive
awareness will develop of what is most suitable for a
particular person. For kyo types (low or deficient in energy), a gentle and sensitive touch is required, and any
stretched positions can be maintained for a longer time
as this will bring more energy to that part of the body.
Pressure, held by the thumb or palm, can also be maintained for an increased length of time, approximately
10-15 seconds. For jitsu types (high or excess energy),
the stretches can be done quite quickly so that the energy is dispersed, and also shaking or rocking areas of
the body can have the same effect. The pressure that is

exerted by the thumbs or palms should also be held for a shorter length of time, so that excess energy is dispelled.

Body reading
It is possible for practitioners of shiatsu, as they become increasingly experienced, to assess a person's physical and mental state of health by observing the body and forming accurate observations. If the traditional ways of Eastern diagnosis are studied, this can assist greatly. The Eastern methods were based on the senses of hearing, seeing, smelling and touching and also by questioning people to obtain information leading to an overall diagnosis. This is known as body reading.

Makko-ho exercises
Makko-ho exercises are six stretching exercises, each of which affects one pair of the meridians by stimulating its flow of energy. If the complete set of exercises is performed, all the body's meridians will have been stimulated in turn, which should result in increased vigour and an absence of tiredness. Before beginning the exercises, you should feel calm and relaxed. It may prove beneficial to perform some abdominal breathing first (as previously described).

One example is the *triple heater and heart governor*

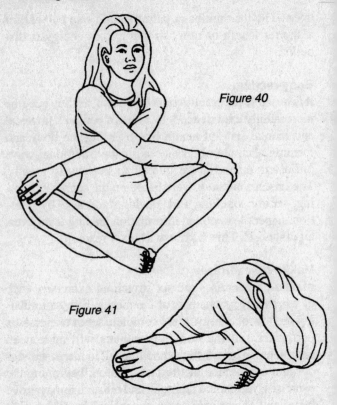

Figure 40

Figure 41

Figure 42

meridian stretch. Sit on the ground with either the feet together or crossed. The right hand should grasp the left knee and the left hand the right knee, both quite firmly (*see* figure 40). Then inhale and, as you exhale, lean forwards and downwards with the top half of the body so that the knees are pushed apart (*see* figure 41). Hold this position for approximately 30 seconds while breathing normally, and then, after inhaling, return to the upright position.

For the *large intestine and lung stretch*, stand with feet apart, hands clasped by the thumbs behind the back, and bend forward keeping the arms straight out behind you (figure 42). Then bring the clasped hands as far forward over your head as you can manage, breathing out at this point. Then after retaining the position for about 30 seconds, straighten up and inhale.

The *stomach and spleen stretch* involves kneeling flat on the floor with the knees to the side a little to allow your bottom to also touch the floor (if possible – if not sit on a cushion). On breathing out lean back, supporting yourself on your arms (figure 43). If this feels comfortable and you think you could not stretch backwards any further, that's fine. If you are more supple and can go back further, then do so, but only as far as you feel comfortable. The position will vary with the individual but some will be able to stretch all the way until laying

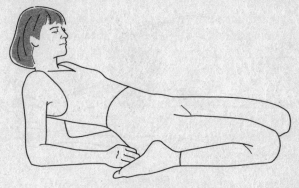

Figure 43

on the floor with the arms outstretched beyond the head. Whichever stage is comfortable for you, hold it for around thirty seconds.

The *bladder and kidney stretch* is performed sitting on the floor with legs together. Bending forward, reach out and clasp your feet (or as far you can reach) and drop your head forward towards your knees (figure 44). Stay like this for about thirty seconds breathing gently, then breathe in as you resume the sitting position.

The *small intestine and heart stretch* (figure 45 is performed by sitting with the soles of the feet together, the knees pointing out, with the elbows outside the legs.) Bend forward at the waist so that the head moves to or

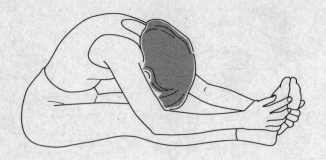

Figure 44

Figure 45

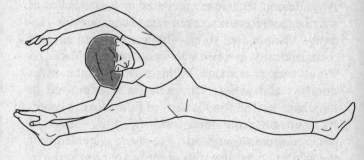

Figure 46

near to the feet and at the same time breath out. Stay like this for thirty seconds, breathing gently, then straighten up while breathing in.

The last of these six exercises is the *liver and gall bladder stretch*. The legs should be spread wide, while sitting on the floor and then from the waist the body is bent to one side while the arm goes over the head. The other arm reaches for the foot (figure 46). After holding, this is repeated in the other direction before straightening.

After completion of all exercises, lie flat on the ground for several minutes and relax.

Moxibustion

An additional technique often used in shiatsu is that of moxibustion. Heat has certain natural connotations – security, warmth, and so on. The warmth is often used therapeutically, as when a hot water bottle is placed on a sore back or stomach. In this way, heat often gives comfort and relief. This benefit is exploited in moxibustion. The word is derived from moxa, a down-like substance obtained from the dried leaves of *Artemisia moxa* (mugwort). The moxa is burned near the skin and cigar-like rolls of moxa are produced specifically for this purpose. The heat is applied to a certain area or tsubo (acupuncture point) and it is very helpful for chronic conditions and in treating conditions such as arthritis, rheumatism, asthma, menstrual pains and it is useful in promoting good circulation.

The technique involves lighting the end of the moxa roll until it is glowing red and the hot end is then held near the point of treatment. The roll can be moved in circles above the point or simply placed at the point, removed, replaced, and so on. The heat source should not be placed nearer than 2–3 cm from the skin and the heat should not be allowed to build up to the point of discomfort. The treatment can last for up to 10 minutes for each area or acupuncture point.

There are obvious safeguards of which to beware. In

addition to limiting time over and distance from the point, ash from the moxa should not fall on the recipient. Also, the technique should not be used on the face, nor is it appropriate on the body of a pregnant woman – although it is quite acceptable for it to be used on the legs and arms in this latter case. As a complementary procedure to shiatsu, moxibustion is very useful, commonly after the shiatsu treatment is finished, and if certain areas of the body need further treatment.

Tsubos

As mentioned previously, tsubos are the points used in acupuncture and acupressure. Shiatsu can be applied to one of these points to influence the energy flow along the meridian upon which the tsubo lies. There are various links between tsubos and organs elsewhere in the body and a tsubo will often influence the energy in the area around the point treated. Thus a particular tsubo can be focused upon because it lies on the meridian which links to the organ in question. There are numerous publications that show maps of the meridians and the tsubos and the link between the points and the effect that treatment at this point will have. While it is not possible here to provide a comprehensive listing, some examples are given to show how it works.

When tsubos are used, both sides of the body should

be treated and the points held for up to two minutes. The pressure should be applied directly down on to the body and not at an angle, to ensure that the full effect is gained. The maps enable the point to be found, if only approximately, and it is then a matter of gently feeling around the point until it is felt that it has been found. Sometimes there may be a small dip, or it may feel obvious. Quite often the tsubos are included in the complete shiatsu treatment or to restore the balance or help a particular. Also, while performing shiatsu, places may be found where it is felt some pressure on the point would help, and these can be compared with the body maps to check on their function.

As an example let us look at the meridians and associated tsubos on the arm, as viewed from the back. Figure 47 shows the basic arm structure, with tsubos and meridians. It should be mentioned here that when defining the actual position of the tsubos, a particular unit, the cun, is used. This is defined as follows:

- 1 cun is the greatest width of the recipient's thumb
- 3 cun is the width of four fingers, and
- 1^1/$_2$ cun is about the width of the first two fingers.

Other measures, e.g. 2 cun have to be estimated from these.

Referring to figure 47, the meridians are marked by dashed lines. From the outer arm these are the large

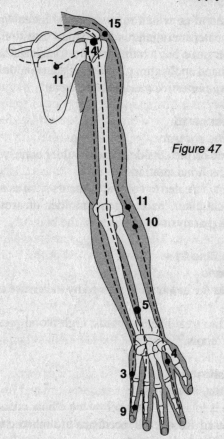

Figure 47

intestine meridian which runs along the index finger; the triple heater meridian; and the small intestine meridian. Each tsubo has a number and a translated name, with the related application. Starting at the shoulder and with the large intestine meridian, we have:

Large intestine 15
Corner of the shoulder
This is found on the outside of the shoulder bone, where there is a small indentation.

This point is treated to combat ailments such as a stiff or frozen shoulder, pain in the shoulder or arm and hemiplegia (paralysis of one side of the body).

Large intestine 11
Crooked pond
This point is the indentation formed by the crease of the elbow.

It is used to treat haemorrhoids, high blood pressure and tennis elbow.

Large intestine 10
Arm (or hand) three miles
This tsubo is located 1 cun below the elbow crease.

This is used for overall good health and to combat aching arms and sore throats.

Large intestine 4
Joining of the valleys
This is found on the small rise of flesh created when the thumb is pushed in to the index finger.

This is also used for overall good health (but should not be used on a recipient who is pregnant). In addition it is used for aches in the head, particularly to the front, and also it helps balance the intestines.

The large intestine meridian has a further point on the face, near the nose. Next, turning to the middle meridian of the three, the triple heater:

Triple heater 14
Top of shoulder
This is located just to the back of the top of the shoulder bone.

This tsubo is for dealing with pain in the shoulder.

Triple heater 5
Outer gate
This is located 2 cun above the crease of the wrist.

It is used for combating migraine, ear problems including tinnitus and colds.

The triple heater has one further point, around the eye. The final meridian is the small intestine meridian.

Small intestine 11
Centre of heaven

This is located roughly in the centre of the shoulder blade.

It is used for shoulder problems, such as pain or a stiff shoulder and also for lung ailments and any pain associated with the ribs muscles.

Small intestine 3
Back stream

This is located just beneath the base of the little finger on the edge of the hand.

It is used for hearing problems such as poor hearing, ringing and so on. Also for numbness in the fingers.

The final small intestine tsubo is also on the head, around the ear lobe. The last point on the arm number 9, is a heart point, *Little rushing in*, which is for heart complaints such as angina, heart attack and also anxiety.

Common Complaints

Perhaps one of the commonest ailments associated with the modern lifestyle is concerned with digestion. The so-called western diet, as mentioned earlier, is considered to be unsuitable in terms of its high saturated fat and sugar content and many gastric conditions can be traced to diet. Below is provided a brief descriptive summary of the digestive system and some of the conditions and problems encountered, and then we look at what shiatsu and the associated therapies and guidelines suggest.

The digestive system

Before the nutrition in food can be used by the body it has to be broken down into molecules small enough to be transported by the blood and passed into the interstitial tissues and cells. This breakdown of food is achieved by digestion which involves both mechanical and chemical actions and takes place in a long canal which stretches from the mouth to the anus.

The mouth is involved with the mechanical and chemical breakdown of food. The teeth are bony structures

embedded in the jawbone which break food down into
smaller pieces through chewing, or mastication. Each
tooth has three basic portions: the crown, the neck and
the root. The crown is the visible part of the tooth and is
covered in enamel which is the hardest substance in the
body. Beneath the enamel is the dentine, a bony connective tissue which lends shape to the tooth. The pulp
cavity which lies beneath the dentine contains blood
vessels, nerves and lymphatic vessels which run downwards through the root of the tooth. The neck of the
tooth forms the division between the crown and the root
and is bordered by the gum. The root also consists of
dentine covered by a bony substance called cementum
which attaches to a ligament which is the anchor of the
tooth.

The first set of human teeth, the milk teeth, begin to
break through the gum at around 6 months after birth
and are gradually lost and replaced by the permanent
set up to the age of 12. The permanent dental set consists of 32 teeth which consist of the following:

- eight incisors – for cutting food
- four canines – for tearing food
- eight premolars – for grinding food
- twelve molars – for grinding food (the third molars
  are also known as the wisdom teeth).

The tongue is a muscular organ anchored to the floor

of the mouth which assists in the breakdown of food and which contains the taste buds.

While food is being chewed and broken into smaller pieces, it is also mixed with saliva which is continuously secreted into the mouth from the salivary glands. The amount of saliva secreted increases when food is in the mouth moistening and dissolving the food to facilitate swallowing and beginning the process of chemical breakdown. Water is the main constituent of saliva but it also contains a number of other substances including two digestive enzymes which begin the breakdown of starches.

Saliva is secreted via ducts from three main pairs of glands: the parotid glands, the submandibular glands and the sublingual glands. These glands continue to secrete heavily saliva for a while after food has been swallowed to wash out the mouth and dilute substances that may remain.

The oesophagus

Once food leaves the mouth it is a soft substance which can be easily swallowed and passed into the pharynx and then into the oesophagus, the long, hollow, muscular tube that leads to the stomach.

The oesophagus measures approximately 25cm in length and descends through the thoracic cavity in to the abdomen. It functions only as a pathway for food, pushing it onwards through persistent, involuntary muscular movements known as peristalsis. These wave-like movements involve the contraction and relaxation of circular muscles and are assisted by the secretion of mucus from the inner wall of the oesophagus which lubricates the food. Food takes a few seconds to pass through the oesophagus while fluids and soft foods take approximately one second.

Between the main portion of the oesophagus and the stomach there is a slight narrowing where a sphincter muscle is situated. The relaxation of this muscle enables food to be passed into the stomach.

The stomach
The stomach is a large, curved sac-like organ, situated immediately below the diaphragm which consist of four main areas: the cardia, the fundus, the body and the pylorus. The layers of the stomach consist of an outer membrane, three different kinds of muscle fibre, a layer of tissue containing blood vessels and an inner mucosal layer that lies in folds when the stomach is empty but stretches to become smooth when full.

When the food enters the stomach it is stimulated into peristaltic movement and into the release of gastric juice from the gastric glands that lie in the mucous membrane.

The gastric juice contains hydrochloric acid and digestive enzymes, which along with gentle peristaltic movements, further break up the food and turn it into a semi-liquid mixture known as chyme. This process can take up to six hours depending on the amount and type of food eaten, for example carbohydrates will be broken up more quickly than proteins. Once the process is complete the chyme is emptied into the duodenum which forms the first portion of the small intestine.

The intestines
Chemical digestion in the small intestine also involves secretions from three organs that actually lie outside the digestive tract: the pancreas, the liver and the gallbladder.

Once the chyme reaches the duodenum, it stimulates the mucous membrane to secrete the hormone secretin which is then transported via the circulation to the pancreas. The pancreas lies behind the outer curved section of the stomach and is joined to the duodenum by two ducts, the pancreatic duct (which joins the common bile duct from the liver and gallbladder) and the accessory duct. The pancreas is composed of small groups of glandular cells some of which are the islets of Langerhans which are involved in the endocrine function of insulin release. The majority of the cell groups produce a fluid which is a mixture of water, salts, sodium bicarbonate and enzymes which digest triglyceride fats, proteins and carbohydrates. The pancreatic juice is conveyed to the small intestine by the two ducts.

The liver contributes to the digestive process with the production and secretion of bile which is a yellow-green fluid consisting of water, bile salts and bile pigments but no enzymes. Bile salts are active in the breakdown and absorption of the fat substance triglyceride. The liver secretes bile into the gallbladder which stores and concentrates the substance prior to releasing it into the small intestine through the common bile duct. The gallbladder secretes bile in response to stimulation from the hormone cholecystokinin which is secreted by the mucous membrane of the small intestine.

Intestinal juice secreted by the glands in the walls of the small intestine and the submucosal layer of the duodenum also contain digestive enzymes and mucous which helps to neutralise the gastric acid in chyme. Most digestion and absorption of nutrients is completed in the small intestine and the anatomy of the organ is entirely appropriate to this. This muscular tube comprises three portions: the duodenum which measures approximately 25 cm in length, the jejunum, measuring approximately 1 metre and the ileum which is approximately 2 metres in length and extends into the large intestine. The small intestine consists of the same four layers as the stomach but contain, small hair-like projections, known as villi, on the mucosal layers that increase the surface area available for digestion and absorption of nutrients. The villi has a central core which is served by an arteriole, a venule and a capillary network, through which nutrients are passed from the small intestine and into the blood or lymphatic fluid.

Chyme is passed through the small intestine in peristaltic movements but these are far more gentle that those of the upper part of the digestive tract and food tends to remain in the small intestine for a longer period. Chyme is passed on to the large intestine via the ileocaecal valve which is the junction between the ileum and the first portion of the large intestine, the caecum. At this stage the chyme is still a liquid substance but as it travels on from the caecum and through the long portion known as the colon, water and some vitamins are absorbed into the blood and the chyme becomes a more solid mass, faeces. The mucosal layer of the colon also secretes mucus to lubricate the faeces as it is pushed through in gentle peristaltic movements. Although no enzymes are secreted, bacteria that live in the colon convert proteins into amino acids and will produce flatus (wind) from the fermentation of carbohydrates.

The faeces is then passed into the rectum through the

mass peristaltic movement which begins in the transverse portion of the colon in response to involuntary nerve impulses which are stimulated by arrival of food in the stomach. This reflex, known as the gastrocolic response, initiates the contraction of muscles along the intestinal tract which along with voluntary muscular contractions propel the faeces along. The final portion of the intestinal tract, the anus consists of an internal and external sphincter. The internal sphincter relaxes in response to involuntary muscular contraction and the external sphincter, the portion which opens on to the body surface, in response to voluntary muscular control. Once the external sphincter is relaxed the faeces is then expelled from the body.

Ailments afflicting the digestive system
Although not exhaustive, here are some of the conditions, diseases and ailments that can affect some part of the digestive system. Each is described briefly:

colic spasmodic, severe abdominal pain that occurs in waves with brief interludes in between. Intestinal colic is usually the result of the presence of some indigestible food, which causes the contraction of the intestinal muscles. Infantile colic, common in young babies, is caused by wind associated with feeding. An attack of colic is generally not serious but can result in a twisting of the bowel, which must receive immediate medical attention. Colic-type pain may also be caused by an obstruction in the bowel, such as a tumour, which again requires early medical treatment.

colitis inflammation of the colon, the symptoms of which include abdominal pain and diarrhoea, sometimes bloodstained. Ulcerative colitis tends to affect young adults and usually occurs periodically over a number of years. There is abdominal discomfort, fever, frequent watery diarrhoea containing mucus and blood, and anaemia. The condition can be fatal but usually there is a gradual recovery. Treatment is by means of bed rest, drug treatment with corticosteroids and iron supplements, and a bland, low roughage diet. Colitis may be the result of infections caused by the organism *Entamoeba histolytica* (amoebic colitis) and by bacteria (infective colitis).

constipation the condition in which the bowels are opened too infrequently and the faeces become dry, hard and difficult and painful to pass. The frequency of normal bowel opening varies in people but when constipation becomes a problem, it is usually a result of inattention to this habit or to the diet. To correct the condition, a change of lifestyle may be needed, including taking more exercise and increasing fluids and roughage in the diet. Laxatives and enemas are also used to alleviate the condition. Constipation is also a symptom of the more serious condition of blockage of the bowel (by a tumour), but this is less common.

diarrhoea increased frequency and looseness of bowel movement, involving the passage of unusually soft faeces. Diarrhoea can be caused by food poisoning, colitis, irritable bowel syndrome, dysentery, etc. A severe case will result in the loss of water and salts, which must be replaced, and antidiarrhoeal drugs are used in certain circumstances.

diverticulitis inflammation of diverticula (sac-like protrusions through the intestine wall, many of which usually develop later in life and are thought to be related to dietary factors) in the large intestine. During the condition, there are cramp-like pains in the left side of the abdomen, possibly with constipation and fever. Treatment normally involves complete rest with no solid food, and antibiotics.

flatulence a build-up of gas in the stomach or bowels that is released through the mouth or anus.

gastric ulcer an erosion of the stomach mucosa caused by such agents as acid and bile. It may penetrate the muscle and perforate the stomach wall. Typical symptoms include burning pain, belching and possibly nausea when the stomach is empty or soon after eating. Relief may be found with antacid compounds, but surgery may be necessary.

gastritis inflammation of the stomach lining (mucosa). It may be caused by bacteria or excessive alcohol intake.

haemorrhoids (*or* **piles)** varicose and inflamed veins around the lower end of the bowel, situated in the wall of the anus. They are classified as internal, external and mixed, depending on whether they appear beyond the anus. They are commonly caused by constipation or diarrhoea, especially in middle and older age, and may be exacerbated by a sedentary lifestyle. They may also occur as a result of childbearing. Symptoms of haemorrhoids are bleeding and pain, and treatment is by means of creams, injections and suppositories. Attention to diet (to treat constipation) and regular exercise are important, but in severe cases, surgery to remove the haemorrhoids may be necessary.

hernia the protrusion of a part or whole of an organ from out of its normal position within the body cavity. Most commonly, a hernia involves part of the bowel. A congenital hernia is present at birth, a common one being an umbilical hernia in which abdominal organs protrude into the umbilical cord. This is the result of a failure during foetal development and can be corrected by surgery. An acquired hernia occurs after birth, a common example being an inguinal hernia, in which part of the bowel bulges through a weak part of the abdominal wall (known as the inguinal canal). Another common type is a hiatus hernia, in which the stomach passes through the hiatus (a hole allowing passage of the oesophagus), from the abdomen into the chest cavity. A reducible hernia is freely movable and can be returned by manipulation into its rightful place. An irreducible hernia describes the opposite situation, and an incarcerated hernia is one that has become swollen and fixed in its position. An obstructed hernia is one involving the bowel. The contents of the hernia are unable to pass farther down and are held up and obstructed.

The most dangerous situation is a strangulated hernia, in which the blood supply has been cut off because of the protrusion itself. This becomes painful and eventually gangrenous and requires immediate surgery. Strenuous physical activity can lead to a hernia, which usually develops gradually. Although short-term measures are employed to control a hernia or reduce its size, the usual treatment is by means of surgery to return and retain the protrusion in its proper place.

indigestion (*or* **dyspepsia**) discomfort in the upper abdomen or lower chest after eating, with heartburn, nausea and flatulence accompanying a feeling of fullness. The causes are numerous and include gallstones, peptic ulcer, hiatus hernia and diseases of the liver or pancreas.

irritable bowel syndrome a condition caused by abnormal muscular contractions (or increased motility) in the colon, producing effects in the large and small intestines. Symptoms include pain in the abdomen, which changes location, disturbed bowel movements with diarrhoea then normal movements or constipation, heartburn and a bloated feeling caused by wind. The specific cause is unknown and no disease is present, so treatment is limited to relief of anxiety or stress (which may be contributory factors) and also some drug therapy to reduce muscle activity and careful choice of diet to include a high fibre content.

peptic ulcer an ulcer in the stomach (gastric ulcer), oesophagus, duodenum (duodenal ulcer) or jejunum. It is caused by a break in the mucosal lining as a result of the action of acid and pepsin (an enzyme active in protein breakdown), either because of their high concentrations or other factors affecting the mucosal protective mechanisms.

Treatment of digestive complaints

In all cases, the complete shiatsu body routine will help by removing energy blockages and generally improving the body's condition. Particular areas to concentrate upon are the middle and lower back, and the abdomen. A circular rubbing with the palm and heel of the hand will help the circulation. On the abdomen, more of a kneading motion can be used as well, followed by a gentle finger-tip pressure, applied around an imaginary circle on the abdomen (as mentioned previously). For complaints related more to the stomach, the area around the navel should be pressed gently with the palm and then the whole area up to the ribs using the thumbs. Each application of pressure should be for about five seconds.

In addition to the general application of shiatsu, certain tsubos can be targeted. The specific ones (as opposed to those used for general good health) are as follows:

- Large intestine 11   for haemorrhoids
- Stomach 25   for stomach pain, bowel and intestinal problems
- Stomach 44   for stomach pain
- Bladder 25   for constipation or diarrhoea, bloated feeling
- Bladder 27   for all small intestine complaints
- Conception vessel 14   for stomach ulcers

Most of these acupressure points are quite easy to find. Figure 47 illustrates the position of Large intestine 11. Stomach 25 is located 2 cun on each side of the navel while Stomach 44 is between the second and third toe. Bladder 25 and 27 are more difficult to find initially and require reference to an anatomical drawing. Figure 48 shows the positions as closely as possible. Conception vessel 14 is 1 cun beneath the base of the breastbone.

Moxibustion (*see* earlier) can be used to good effect for the majority of these ailments. The following tsubos should receive attention (but others listed above can also be used): Stomach 36; Heart governor 6; Conception vessel 14; and Bladder 21. These are located as follows: Stomach 36 is 3 cun beneath the knee in a small hollow next to the tibia; Heart governor 6 is in the middle of the width of the arm about 2 cun above the wrist; the location of Conception vessel 14 is described above; and Bladder 21 is just a small distance above Bladder 25 (about the same distance as 25 is above 27) on the lower back.

As will be gathered a vital tool in combating illnesses and conditions of this nature is the implementation of a good and appropriate diet. Fundamental guidelines to follow include increasing the amount of fibre taken in. This will help the body in general, not just the digestive system. Whole wheat and other grains such as oats,

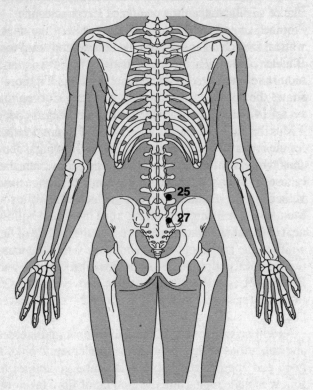

Figure 48 – tsubos and the bladder

brown rice and so on, are ideal. In addition, regular intake of vegetables, pulses and fruits are important.

At the same time, avoid too much of the high protein, high fat foods. In general cut down on the consumption of meat (particularly red meat), high fat dairy products, and also consider reducing alcohol intake and if appropriate, spicy foods. Desserts that look attractive are often full of calories and actually do as much harm as good. It is useful to check on calorie intake but even then the correct types of food must be eaten. The following sections provide helpful reference information on calorific value of foods, their fat and fibre content. These are useful in ensuring that a balanced diet is achieved.

Nutritional Information

General advice on diet has been mentioned earlier. As an overall policy, a nutritionally sound diet is said by some to comprise the 'food pyramid'. This represents the fact that the largest part of the diet, the base (between 30 and 45%) should be made up of wholegrains. Next comes vegetables, comprising 15 to 20%, then 10 to 15% fruit and finally less than 5% fats and sweets. It is recommended that 25 to 35 grams of fibre is consumed each day. Some experts would advocate 40 to 50 grams. The following tables enable some appreciation of these quantities to be gained. A good guide is also to eat foods that have less than 20% of their calories coming from fat (1 gram of fat = 9 calories). In this way by reducing the bad components of your diet, concentrating on the healthier items and combining this with shiatsu exercises, your health will improve.

Dietary Data

Cereals and Cereal Products

Food Item	Amount	Kcals	Carb	Prot	Fat	Fibre
Biscuits						
Cheddars, mini	100g	534	52.9	11.3	30.2	2.3
Cheeselets	100g	464	56.9	10.3	21.7	N
Cheeselets	1 biscuit	5	0.6	0.1	3.3	N
Chocolate, assorted	100g	524	67.4	5.7	27.6	2.9
Club, mint	100g	521	58.9	3.8	30.0	N
Club, mint	1 biscuit	133	15.1	1.0	7.7	N
Club, double choc	100g	539	59.3	5.1	29.8	N
Club, double choc	1 biscuit	127	14.0	1.2	7.0	N
Digestive	100g	471	68.6	6.3	24.1	4.6
Digestive	1 biscuit	73	9.8	1.0	3.3	0.6
Digestive with plain chocolate	100g	511	60.8	7.6	26.1	3.1

127

Food Item	Amount	Kcals	Carb	Prot	Fat	Fibre
Digestive with plain chocolate	1 biscuit	85	10.0	1.3	4.4	0.5
Flapjacks	100g	484	60.4	4.5	26.6	2.6
Garibaldis	100g	409	70.5	4.0	9.4	N
Garibaldis	1 biscuit	45	7.3	0.4	1.0	N
Gingernut	100g	456	79.1	5.6	15.2	4.7
Hob nobs	100g	490	65.3	7.1	21.9	N
Hob nobs	1 biscuit	72	9.6	1.0	3.2	N
Homemade	100g	463	64.3	6.2	21.9	1.8
Jaffa cakes	100g	363	67.8	3.5	10.5	0.6
Sandwich	100g	513	69.2	5.0	25.9	1.1
Semi-sweet	100g	457	74.8	6.7	16.6	2.1
Short-sweet	100g	469	62.2	6.2	23.4	1.5
Wafer, filled	100g	535	66.0	4.7	29.9	1.4
Oatcakes	100g	441	63.0	10.0	18.3	3.6
Shortbread	100g	498	63.9	5.9	26.1	2.2
Bran						
Wheat	100g	206	26.8	14.1	5.5	39.6
Wheat	1 tbsp [7g]	14	1.9	1.0	0.4	2.7

Food Item	Amount	Kcals	Carb	Prot	Fat	Fibre
Bread						
Brown, average	100g	218	44.3	8.5	2.0	5.9
Brown, average	25g slice	55	1.8	2.0	0.5	1.5
Chapatis, made with fat	100g	328	48.3	8.1	12.8	7.0
Chapatis, made with fat	1 [60g]	197	29.0	4.9	7.7	4.2
Chapatis, made without fat	100g	202	43.7	7.3	1.0	6.4
Chapatis, made without fat	1 [55g]	111	24.0	4.0	0.6	3.5
Croissants	100g	360	38.3	8.3	20.3	2.5
Croissants	1, average plain [50g]	180	19.2	4.2	10.2	1.3
Crumpets, toasted	100g	199	43.4	6.7	1.0	2.9
Crumpets, toasted	1 [40g]	80	17.4	2.7	0.4	1.2
Currant	100g	289	50.7	7.5	7.6	3.8
Currant	30g slice	87	15.2	2.3	2.3	1.1
Granary	100g	235	46.3	9.3	2.7	6.5
Granary	25g slice	59	11.6	2.3	0.7	1.6
Hovis	100g	212	41.5	9.5	2.0	5.1
Hovis	25g slice	53	10.4	2.4	0.5	1.3
Malt	100g	268	56.8	8.3	2.4	6.5

Food Item	Amount	Kcals	Carb	Prot	Fat	Fibre
Malt	35g slice	94	19.9	2.9	0.8	2.3
Naan	100g	336	50.1	8.9	12.5	2.2
Pitta	100g	265	57.9	9.2	1.2	3.9
Pitta	75g pitta	199	43.4	6.9	0.9	2.9
Pitta	95g pitta	252	55.0	8.7	1.1	3.7
Rolls, brown, crusty	100g	255	50.4	10.3	2.8	7.1
Rolls, brown, crusty	1 roll [48g]	122	22.7	4.9	1.3	3.4
Rolls, brown, soft	100g	268	51.8	10.0	2.8	6.4
Rolls, brown, soft	1 roll [43g]	115	22.3	4.3	1.2	2.8
Rolls, hamburger buns	100g	264	48.8	9.1	5.0	4.0
Rolls, hamburger buns	1 roll [50g]	132	24.4	4.6	2.5	2.0
Rolls, white, crusty	100g	280	57.6	10.9	2.3	4.3
Rolls, white, crusty	1 roll [50g]	140	28.8	5.5	1.2	2.2
Rolls, white, soft	100g	268	51.6	9.2	4.2	3.9
Rolls, white, soft	1 roll [45g]	121	23.2	4.4	1.9	1.8
Rolls, wholemeal	100g	241	48.3	9.0	2.9	8.8
Rolls, wholemeal	1 roll [45g]	108	21.7	4.1	1.3	4.0
Rye	100g	219	45.8	8.3	1.7	5.8
Rye	25g slice	55	11.5	2.1	0.4	1.5

Food Item	Amount	Kcals	Carb	Prot	Fat	Fibre
Vitbe	100g	229	43.4	9.7	3.1	5.8
Vitbe	25g slice	57	10.9	2.4	0.8	1.5
White, 'with added fibre'	100g.	230	49.6	7.6	1.5	3.1
White, 'with added fibre'	25g slice	58	12.4	1.9	0.4	0.8
White, average	100g	235	49.3	8.4	1.9	1.5
White, average	25g slice	59	12.3	2.1	0.5	0.4
White, french stick	100g	270	55.4	9.6	2.7	1.5
White, french stick	2 inch stick [40g]	108	22.2	3.8	1.1	0.6
White, fried	100g	503	48.5	7.9	32.2	1.6
White, fried	35g slice	176	17.0	2.8	11.3	0.6
White, sliced	100g	217	46.8	7.6	1.3	1.5
White, sliced	25g slice	54	11.7	1.9	0.3	0.4
Wholemeal, average	100g	215	41.6	9.2	2.5	5.8
Wholemeal, average	25g slice	54	10.4	2.3	0.6	1.5
Breakfast cereals						
All-bran	100g	261	46.6	14.0	3.4	30.0
Bran Flakes	100g	318	69.3	10.2	1.9	17.3
Coco Pops	100g	384	74.0	5.3	1.0	1.1

Food Item	Amount	Kcals	Carb	Prot	Fat	Fibre
Common Sense Oat Bran						
Flakes	100g	357	85.9	11.0	4.0	10.0
Corn Flakes	100g	360	88.6	7.9	0.7	3.4
Crunchy Nut Corn Flakes	100g	398	93.7	7.4	4.0	1.6
Frosties	100g	377	93.7	5.3	0.5	1.2
Fruit 'n Fibre	100g	349	72.1	9.0	4.7	10.1
Muesli with no added sugar	100g	366	67.1	10.5	7.8	10.5
Muesli, Swiss style	100g	363	72.2	9.8	5.9	8.1
Oat and Wheat Bran	100g	325	67.7	10.6	3.5	17.9
Porridge, with milk	100g	116	13.7	4.8	5.1	0.8
Porridge, with water	100g	49	9.0	1.5	1.1	0.8
Puffed Wheat	100g	321	67.3	14.2	1.3	8.8
Raisin Wheats	100g	337	75.4	9.0	2.0	8.0
Ready Brek	100g	373	68.6	11.4	7.8	7.2
Rice Krispies	100g	369	89.7	6.1	0.9	1.1
Ricicles	100g	381	95.7	4.3	0.5	0.9
Shredded Wheat	100g	325	68.3	10.6	3.0	10.1
Shredded Wheat	1 piece [22g]	72	304	15.0	2.3	2.2

Food Item	Amount	Kcals	Carb	Prot	Fat	Fibre
Shreddies	100g	331	74.1	10.1	1.5	10.9
Smacks	100g	386	89.6	8.0	2.0	3.0
Special K	100g	377	81.7	15.3	1.0	2.7
Start	100g	355	81.7	7.9	1.7	5.7
Sugar Puffs	100g	348	84.5	5.9	0.8	4.8
Sultana Bran	100g	303	67.8	8.5	1.6	10.0
Weetabix	100g	352	75.7	11.0	2.7	11.6
Weetabix	1 piece [20g]	70	15.1	2.2	0.5	2.3
Weetaflakes	100g	359	79.3	9.2	2.8	9.7
Weetos	100g	372	86.1	6.1	2.7	5.3
Buns						
Chelsea	100g	366	56.1	7.8	13.8	2.2
Chelsea	1 bun [78g]	285	43.8	6.1	10.8	1.7
Currant	100g	296	52.7	7.6	7.5	1.8
Currant	1 bun [60g]	178	31.6	4.6	4.5	1.1
Hot cross	100g	310	58.5	7.4	6.8	2.2
Hot cross	1 bun [50g]	155	29.3	3.7	3.4	1.1
Cakes						
Battenburg	100g	370	50.0	5.9	17.5	1.5

Food Item	Amount	Kcals	Carb	Prot	Fat	Fibre
Battenburg	40g slice	148	20	2.4	7.0	0.6
Chocolate Krispie, individual	100g	464	73.1	5.6	18.6	0.8
Chocolate Krispie, individual	1 cake [25g]	116	18.3	1.4	4.7	0.2
Doughnuts, jam	100g	336	48.8	5.7	14.5	2.5
Doughnuts, jam	1 [75g]	252	3.4	4.3	10.9	1.9
Doughnuts, ring	100g	397	47.2	6.1	21.7	3.1
Doughnuts, ring	1 [60g]	238	28.3	3.7	13.0	1.9
Eclairs	100g	396	26.1	5.6	30.6	1.5
Eclairs	1 [90g]	356	23.5	5.0	27.5	1.4
Fancy Iced, individual	100g	407	68.8	3.8	14.9	2.2
Fancy Iced, individual	1 cake [30g]	122	20.6	1.1	4.5	0.7
Fruit, plain	100g	354	57.9	5.1	12.9	2.5
Fruit, plain	90g slice	319	52.1	4.6	11.6	2.2
Fruit, rich	100g	341	59.6	3.8	11.0	3.2
Fruit, rich	70g slice	239	41.7	2.7	7.7	2.2
Fruit, rich, iced	100g	356	62.7	4.1	11.4	3.1
Fruit, rich, iced	70g slice	249	43.9	2.9	8.0	2.2
Fruit, wholemeal	100g	363	52.8	6.0	15.7	3.0

Food Item	Amount	Kcals	Carb	Prot	Fat	Fibre
Fruit, wholemeal	90g slice	327	47.5	5.4	14.1	2.7
Gateau	100g	337	43.4	5.7	16.8	0.5
Gateau	85g slice	286	36.9	4.8	14.3	0.4
Madeira	100g	393	58.4	5.4	16.9	1.3
Madeira	40g slice	157	23.4	2.2	6.8	0.5
Sponge, basic	100g	459	52.4	6.4	26.3	1.0
Sponge, basic	53g slice	243	22.5	2.8	11.3	0.5
Sponge, fatless	100g	294	53.0	10.1	6.1	1.0
Sponge, fatless	53g slice	156	28.1	5.4	3.2	0.5
Sponge, jam filled	100g	302	64.2	4.2	4.9	1.1
Sponge, jam filled	65g slice	196	41.7	2.7	3.2	0.7
Sponge, butter icing	100g	490	52.4	4.5	30.6	0.7
Sponge, butter icing	65g slice	319	34.1	2.9	19.9	0.5
Swiss Rolls, chocolate, individual	100g	337	58.1	4.3	11.3	2.5
Swiss Rolls, chocolate, individual	1 roll [26g]	88	16.3	1.2	2.9	0.7
Teacakes	100g	329	58.3	8.9	8.3	4.7
Teacakes	1 [60g]	197	35.0	5.3	5.0	2.8

Food Item	Amount	Kcals	Carb	Prot	Fat	Fibre
Crackers						
Cream	100g	440	68.3	9.5	16.3	2.2
Cream	1 [7g]	31	4.8	0.7	1.1	0.2
Wholemeal	100g	413	72.1	10.1	11.3	4.8
Wholemeal	1 [15g]	62	10.8	1.5	1.7	0.7
Crispbread						
Rye	100g	321	70.6	9.4	2.1	11.6
Rye	1 [10g]	32	7.1	0.9	0.2	1.2
Custard powder	100g	354	92.0	0.6	0.7	0.1
Flour						
Chapatis brown	100g	333	73.7	11.5	1.2	10.3
Chapatis, brown	1 level tbsp [20g]	67	14.7	2.3	0.2	2.1
Chapatis white	100g	335	77.6	9.8	0.5	4.1
Chapatis, white	1 level tbsp [20g]	67	15.5	2.0	0.1	0.8
Cornflour	100g	354	92.0	0.6	0.7	0.1
Cornflour	1 level tbsp [20g]	71	18	0.1	0.1	trace
Rye flour	100g	335	75.9	8.2	2.0	11.7
Rye flour	1 level tbsp [20g]	67	15.2	1.6	0.4	2.3

Food Item	Amount	Kcals	Carb	Prot	Fat	Fibre
Soya, full fat	100g	447	23.5	36.8	23.5	10.7
Soya, full fat	1 level tbsp [20g]	89	4.7	7.4	4.7	2.1
Soya, low fat	100g	352	28.2	45.3	7.2	13.3
Soya, low fat	1 level tbsp [20g]	70	5.6	9.1	1.4	2.7
Wheat , brown	100g	323	68.5	12.6	1.8	7.0
Wheat, brown	1 level tbsp [20g]	65	13.7	2.5	0.4	1.4
Wheat, white, breadmaking	100g	341	75.3	11.5	1.4	3.7
Wheat, white, breadmaking	1 level tbsp [20g]	68	15.1	2.3	0.5	0.7
Wheat, white, plain	100g	341	77.7	9.4	1.3	3.6
Wheat, white, plain	1 level tbsp [20g]	68	15.5	1.9	0.3	0.7
Wheat, white, self-raising	100g	330	75.6	8.9	1.2	4.1
Wheat, white, self-raising	1 level tbsp [20g]	66	15.1	1.8	0.2	0.8
Wheat, wholemeal	100g	310	63.9	12.7	2.2	8.6
Wheat, wholemeal	1 level tbsp [20g]	62	12.8	2.5	0.4	1.7
Noodles						
Egg, raw	100g	391	71.7	12.1	8.2	5.0
Egg, boiled	100g	62	13.0	2.2	0.5	1.0
Egg, boiled	300g packet	186	39	6.6	1.5	3.0

Food Item	Amount	Kcals	Carb	Prot	Fat	Fibre
Oatmeal, raw	100g	375	66.0	11.2	9.2	6.8
Pancakes						
Scotch	100g	292	43.6	5.8	11.7	1.6
Scotch	1, [50g]	146	21.8	2.9	5.9	0.8
Pasta						
Macaroni, raw	100g	348	75.8	12.0	1.8	5.0
Macaroni, boiled	100g	86	18.5	3.0	0.5	1.5
Spaghetti, white, raw	100g	342	74.1	12.0	1.8	5.1
Spaghetti, white, boiled	100g	104	22.2	3.6	0.7	1.8
Spaghetti, wholemeal, raw	100g	324	66.2	13.4	2.5	11.5
Spaghetti, wholemeal, boiled	100g	113	23.2	4.7	0.9	4.0
Fresh egg pasta	100g	270	49.9	10.5	3.2	1.5
Fresh spinach pasta	100g	278	50.9	10.6	3.5	1.5
Dried spinach pasta	100g	37	75.2	12.8	1.7	1.5
Pastries						
Cream Horns	100g	435	25.8	3.8	35.8	1.0
Cream Horns	1 [60g]	261	15.5	2.3	21.5	0.6
Custard tarts, individual	100g	277	32.4	6.3	14.5	1.2

Food Item	Amount	Kcals	Carb	Prot	Fat	Fibre
Custard tarts, individual	1 [94g]	260	30.5	5.9	13.6	1.1
Danish	100g	374	51.3	5.8	17.6	2.7
Danish	1, medium [110g]	411	56.4	6.4	19.4	3.0
Eccles cakes	100g	475	59.3	3.9	26.4	2.0
Eccles cakes	1 [45g]	214	26.7	1.8	11.9	0.9
Greek	100g	322	40.0	4.7	17.0	1.9
Jam tarts	100g	380	62.0	3.3	13.0	1.7
Jam tarts	90g slice	342	55.8	3.0	11.7	1.5
Mince pies, individual	100g	423	59.0	4.3	20.4	2.8
Mince pies, individual	1 [48g]	203	28.3	1.2	9.8	1.3
Flaky, raw	100g	424	34.8	4.2	30.7	1.6
Flaky, cooked	100g	560	45.9	5.6	40.6	2.1
Shortcrust, raw	100g	449	46.8	5.7	27.9	2.2
Shortcrust, cooked	100g	521	54.2	6.6	32.3	2.5
Wholemeal, raw	100g	431	38.5	7.7	28.4	5.2
Wholemeal, cooked	100g	499	44.6	8.9	32.9	6.0
Puddings						
Blackcurrant pie, pastry top and bottom	100g	262	34.5	3.1	13.3	4.8

Food Item	Amount	Kcals	Carb	Prot	Fat	Fibre
Blackcurrant pie, pastry top and bottom	120g portion	314	41.4	3.7	16.0	5.8
Bread pudding	100g	297	49.7	5.9	9.6	3.0
Bread pudding	170g portion	505	84.5	10.0	16.3	5.1
Christmas pudding, home-made	100g	291	49.5	4.6	9.7	2.7
Christmas pudding, retail	100g	329	56.3	3.0	11.8	3.4
Crumble, fruit	100g	198	34.0	2.0	6.9	2.2
Crumble, fruit	170g portion	337	57.8	3.4	11.7	3.7
Crumble, fruit, wholemeal	100g	193	31.7	2.6	7.1	3.0
Crumble, fruit, wholemeal	170g portion	328	53.9	4.4	12.1	5.1
Fruit pie, top crust only	100g	186	28.7	2.0	7.9	2.1
Fruit pie, top crust only	120g portion	223	34.4	2.4	9.4	2.5
Fruit pie, pastry top and bottom	100g	260	34.0	3.0	13.3	2.2
Fruit pie, pastry top and bottom	120g portion	312	40.8	3.6	16.0	2.6
Fruit pie, individual	100g	369	56.7	4.3	15.5	2.3
Fruit pie, individual	1 [50g]	185	28.4	2.2	7.8	1.2
Fruit pie, wholemeal, top crust only	100g	183	26.6	2.6	8.1	3.0
Fruit pie, wholemeal,						

Food Item	Amount	Kcals	Carb	Prot	Fat	Fibre
top crust only	120g portion	220	31.9	3.1	9.7	3.6
Fruit pie, wholemeal, pastry top and bottom	100g	251	30.0	4.0	13.6	3.6
Fruit pie, wholemeal, pastry top and bottom	120g slice	301	36	4.8	16.3	4.3
Lemon meringue pie	100g	319	45.9	4.5	14.4	0.8
Lemon meringue pie	120g slice	383	55.1	5.4	17.3	1.0
Pancakes, sweet, made with whole milk	100g	301	35.0	5.9	16.2	0.9
Pancakes, sweet, made with whole milk	110g portion	331	38.5	6.5	17.8	1.0
Pie, with pie filling	100g	273	34.6	3.2	14.5	2.0
Pie, with pie filling	120g portion	328	41.5	3.8	17.4	2.4
Sponge pudding	100g	340	45.3	5.8	16.3	1.2
Sponge pudding	170g portion	578	77	9.8	27.7	2.0
Treacle tart	100g	368	60.4	3.7	14.1	1.4
Treacle tart	120g portion	322	72.5	4.4	16.9	1.7
Rice						
Brown, raw	100g	357	81.3	6.7	2.8	3.8

Food Item	Amount	Kcals	Carb	Prot	Fat	Fibre
Brown, boiled	100g	141	32.1	2.6	1.1	1.5
Savoury, raw	100g	415	77.4	8.4	10.3	4.0
Savoury, cooked	100g	142	26.3	2.9	3.5	1.3
White, easy cook, raw	100g	383	85.8	7.3	3.6	2.7
White, easy cook, boiled	100g	138	30.9	2.6	1.3	1.0
White, fried in lard	100g	131	25.0	2.2	3.2	1.2
Sago						
raw	100g	355	94.0	0.2	0.2	0.5
Savouries						
Dumplings	100g	208	24.5	2.8	11.7	1.4
Macaroni cheese	100g	178	13.6	7.3	10.8	0.8
Macaroni cheese	300g portion	534	40.8	21.9	32.4	2.4
Pancakes, savoury,						
made with whole milk	100g	273	24.0	6.3	17.5	1.0
Ravioli, canned in tomato sauce	100g	70	10.3	3.0	2.2	1.0
Risotto, plain	100g	224	34.4	3.0	9.3	1.3
Samosas, meat	100g	593	17.9	5.1	56.1	1.9
Samosas, vegetable	100g	472	22.3	3.1	41.8	2.4

Food Item	Amount	Kcals	Carb	Prot	Fat	Fibre
Spaghetti						
canned in tomato sauce	100g	64	14.1	1.9	0.4	2.8
Stuffing						
sage and onion	100g	231	20.4	5.2	14.8	2.7
stuffing mix	100g	338	67.2	9.9	5.2	4.7
stuffing mix, made up						
with water	100g	97	19.3	2.8	1.5	1.3
Scones						
Fruit	100g	316	52.9	7.3	9.8	3.6
Plain	100g	362	53.8	7.2	14.6	2.2
Wholemeal	100g	326	43.1	5.8	11.7	5.0
Tapioca						
raw	100g	359	95.0	0.4	0.1	0.4
Wheatgerm	100g	357	44.7	26.7	9.2	15.6
Yorkshire pudding	100g	208	24.7	6.6	9.9	0.9

Nuts and Seeds

Food Item	Amount	Kcals	Carb	Prot	Fat	Fibre
Almonds	100g	612	6.9	21.1	55.8	12.9
	6 whole [10g]	61	0.7	2.1	5.6	1.3
Brazil nuts	100g	682	3.1	14.1	68.2	8.1
	6 whole [20g]	136	0.6	2.8	13.6	1.6
Cashew nuts						
roasted, salted	100g	611	18.8	20.5	50.9	3.2
roasted, salted	10 whole [10g]	61	1.9	2.1	5.1	0.3
roasted, salted	25g packet	153	4.7	5.1	12.7	0.8
Chestnuts	100g	170	36.6	2.0	2.7	6.1
	5 whole [50g]	85	18.3	1.0	1.4	3.0
Coconut						
creamed, block	100g	669	7.0	6.0	68.8	N
dessicated	100g	604	6.4	5.6	62.0	21.1
Hazelnuts	100g	650	6.0	14.1	63.5	8.9
	10 whole [10g]	65	0.6	1.4	6.4	0.9

Food Item	Amount	Kcals	Carb	Prot	Fat	Fibre
Macadamia nuts						
salted	100g	748	4.8	7.9	77.6	5.3
salted	6 nuts [10g]	75	0.5	0.8	7.8	0.5
Mixed nuts						
	100g	607	7.9	22.9	54.1	7.5
	40g packet	243	3.2	9.2	21.6	3.0
	50g packet	304	4.0	11.5	27.1	3.8
Peanuts						
plain	100g	564	12.5	25.6	46.1	7.3
plain	10 whole [10g]	56	1.3	2.6	4.6	0.7
roasted, salted	100g	602	7.1	24.5	53.0	6.9
roasted, salted	10 whole [10g]	60	0.7	2.5	5.3	0.7
roasted, salted	25g packet	151	1.8	6.1	13.3	1.7
roasted, salted	40g packet	241	2.8	9.8	21	2.8
roasted, salted	50g packet	301	3.6	12.3	26.5	3.5
dry roasted	100g	589	10.3	25.5	49.8	7.4
Pecan nuts						
	100g	689	5.8	9.2	70.1	4.7
	3 nuts [18g]	124	1.0	1.7	12.6	0.8
Pine nuts						
	100g	688	4.0	14.0	68.6	1.9

Food Item	Amount	Kcals	Carb	Prot	Fat	Fibre
Pistachio nuts	100g	331	4.6	9.9	30.5	3.3
	10 nuts [8g]	26	0.4	0.8	2.4	0.3
Walnuts	100g	688	3.3	14.7	68.5	5.9
	6 halves [20g]	138	0.7	2.9	13.7	1.2
Nut-based products						
Marzipan, home-made	100g	461	50.2	10.4	25.8	5.8
Marzipan, retail	100g	404	67.6	5.3	14.4	3.2
Peanut butter, smooth	100g	623	13.1	22.6	53.7	6.8
Peanut butter, smooth	generous spreading for bread [20g]	125	2.6	4.5	10.7	1.4
Peanut butter, smooth	thin spreading for bread [12g]	75	1.6	2.7	6.4	0.8
Sesame seeds	100g	578	0.9	18.2	58.0	7.9
	1 tbsp [10g]	58	0.1	1.8	5.8	0.8
Sunflower seeds	100g	581	18.6	19.8	47.5	6.0
	1 tbsp [14g]	81	2.6	2.8	6.7	0.8

Food Item	Amount	Kcals	Carb	Prot	Fat	Fibre
Seed-based products						
Tahini [sesame seed spread]	100g	607	0.9	18.5	58.9	8.0
Tahini [sesame seed spread]	1 heaped tsp [19g]	115	0.2	3.5	11.2	1.5

Vegetables

Food Item	Amount	Kcals	Carb	Prot	Fat	Fibre
Asparagus						
boiled	100g	26	1.4	3.4	0.8	1.4
boiled	5 spears [125g]	33	1.7	4.3	1.0	1.8
raw	100g	25	2.0	2.9	0.6	1.7
Aubergine						
fried in corn oil	100g	302	2.8	1.2	31.9	2.9
raw	100g	15	2.2	0.9	0.4	2.3
Bamboo Shoots						
canned, drained	100g	39	9.7	0.7	0	1.0
canned, drained	225g can	88	21.8	1.6	0	2.3
Beans						
Aduki, dried, boiled	100g	123	22.5	9.3	0.2	5.5
Aduki, dried, boiled	1 tbsp [30g]	37	6.8	2.8	trace	1.7
Baked, canned in tomato sauce	100g	84	15.3	5.2	0.6	6.9
Baked, canned in tomato sauce	1 tbsp [45g]	38	6.9	2.3	0.3	3.1

Food Item	Amount	Kcals	Carb	Prot	Fat	Fibre
Baked, canned in tomato sauce, reduced sugar	100g	73	12.5	5.4	0.6	7.1
Baked, canned in tomato sauce, reduced sugar	1 tbsp [45g]	33	5.6	2.4	0.3	3.2
Blackeye, dried, boiled	100g	116	19.9	8.8	0.7	3.5
Blackeye, dried, boiled	1 tbsp [45g]	52	10.7	4	trace	1.6
Broad, frozen, boiled	100g	81	11.7	7.9	0.6	6.5
Butter, canned, re-heated and drained						
French, frozen, boiled	100g	25	4.7	1.7	0.1	4.1
French, raw	100g	24	3.2	1.9	0.5	2.2
Mung, dried, boiled	100g	91	15.3	7.6	0.4	4.8
Mung, dried, boiled	1 tbsp [30g]	27	4.6	2.3	0.1	1.4
Red kidney, canned, re-heated and drained	100g	100	17.8	6.9	0.6	8.5
Red kidney, dried, boiled	100g	103	17.4	8.4	0.5	9.0
Red kidney, dried, boiled	1 tbsp [30g]	31	5.2	2.5	0.2	2.7
Runner, boiled	100g	186	2.3	1.2	0.5	3.1
Runner, raw	100g	22	3.2	1.6	0.4	2.6
Soya, dried, boiled	100g	141	5.1	14.0	7.3	6.1

Food Item	Amount	Kcals	Carb	Prot	Fat	Fibre
Soya, dried, boiled	1 tbsp [30g]	42	1.5	4.2	2.2	1.8
Beansprouts						
Mung, stir-fried in blended oil	100g	72	2.5	1.9	6.1	3.4
Mung, raw	100g	31	4.0	2.9	0.5	5.6
Beetroot						
boiled	100g	46	9.5	2.3	0.1	2.3
boiled	1 slice [10g]	5	1.0	0.2	trace	0.2
pickled, drained	100g	28	5.6	1.2	0.2	2.5
pickled, drained	1 slice [10g]	3	0.6	0.1	trace	0.3
raw	100g	36	7.6	1.7	0.1	2.8
Black gram	100g	89	13.6	7.8	0.4	5.8
Broccoli						
boiled	100g	24	1.1	3.1	0.8	2.3
raw	100g	33	1.8	4.4	0.9	2.6
Brussels sprouts						
boiled	100g	35	3.5	2.9	1.3	2.6
frozen, boiled	100g	35	2.5	3.5	1.3	4.0
raw	100g	42	4.1	5.3	1.4	3.8

Food Item	Amount	Kcals	Carb	Prot	Fat	Fibre
Cabbage						
boiled	100g	18	2.5	0.8	0.6	2.5
raw	100g	26	4.1	1.7	0.4	2.9
white, raw	100g	27	5.0	1.4	0.2	2.4
Carrots						
canned, re-heated, drained	100g	20	4.2	0.5	0.3	1.9
canned, re-heated, drained	3 medium carrots [35g]	7	1.5	0.2	0.1	0.7
old, boiled	100g	24	4.9	0.6	0.4	2.8
old, raw	100g	35	2.5	0.3	0.2	2.6
young, boiled	100g	22	4.4	0.6	0.4	2.7
young, raw	100g	30	6.0	0.7	0.5	2.6
Cauliflower						
boiled	100g	28	2.1	2.9	0.9	1.6
raw	100g	34	3.0	3.6	0.9	1.9
raw	1 floret [10g]	3	0.3	0.4	trace	0.2
Celery						
boiled	100g	8	0.8	0.5	0.3	2.0
raw	100g	7	0.9	0.5	0.2	1.6

151

Food Item	Amount	Kcals	Carb	Prot	Fat	Fibre
raw	1 stick [30g]	2	0.3	0.2	0.1	0.5
Chick peas						
canned, re-heated, drained	100g	115	16.1	7.2	2.9	4.1
dried, boiled	100g	121	18.2	8.4	2.1	4.8
Chicory						
raw	100g	11	2.8	0.5	0.6	0.9
Courgette						
boiled	100g	19	2.0	2.0	0.4	1.2
fried in corn oil	100g	63	2.6	2.6	4.8	1.2
raw	100g	18	1.8	1.8	0.4	0.9
Cucumber						
raw	100g	10	1.5	0.7	0.1	0.7
raw	1 inch piece [60g]	6	0.9	0.4	0.1	0.4
Curly Kale						
boiled	100g	24	1.0	2.4	1.1	2.6
raw	100g	33	1.4	3.4	1.6	3.3
Fennel						
boiled	100g	11	1.5	0.9	0.2	2.3

Food Item	Amount	Kcals	Carb	Prot	Fat	Fibre
raw	100g	12	1.8	0.9	0.2	2.4
Garlic						
raw	100g	98	16.3	7.9	0.6	4.1
Gherkins						
pickled, drained	100g	14	2.6	0.9	0.1	1.2
Gourd						
raw	100g	11	0.8	1.6	0.2	3.6
Hummus	100g	187	11.6	7.6	12.6	3.2
	1 tbsp [50g]	94	5.8	3.8	6.3	1.6
Leeks						
boiled	100g	21	2.6	1.2	0.7	2.4
boiled	1, medium [160g]	34	4.2	1.9	1.1	3.8
raw	100g	22	2.9	1.6	0.5	2.8
Lentils						
green and brown, whole, dried and boiled	100g	105	16.9	8.8	0.7	3.8
green and brown, whole, boiled, dried & baked	1 tbsp [30g]	32	5.1	2.6	0.2	1.1

153

Food Item	Amount	Kcals	Carb	Prot	Fat	Fibre
red, split, dried, boiled	100g	100	17.5	7.6	0.4	3.3
red, split, dried, boiled	1 tbsp [30g]	30	5.3	2.3	0.1	1.0
Lettuce						
average, raw	100g	14	1.7	0.8	0.5	1.3
average, raw	1 salad-size serving [30g]	4	0.5	0.2	0.2	0.4
iceberg, raw	100g	13	1.9	0.7	0.3	1.3
iceberg, raw	1 salad-size serving [80g]	10	0.6	0.2	0.1	0.4
Marrow						
boiled	100g	9	1.6	0.4	0.2	1.0
raw	100g	12	2.2	0.5	0.2	1.1
Mixed vegetables						
frozen, boiled	100g	42	6.6	3.3	0.5	4.8
with chilli, canned	100g	86	9.1	4.3	3.8	N
with chilli, canned	400g can	345	36.0	17.0	15.0	N
Mushrooms						
boiled	100g	11	0.4	1.8	0.3	2.3
creamed, canned	100g	80	5.4	3.4	5.0	0.7

Food Item	Amount	Kcals	Carb	Prot	Fat	Fibre
creamed, canned	210g can	168	11.3	7.1	10.5	1.5
fried in blended oil	100g	157	0.3	2.4	16.2	3.0
fried in butter	100g	157	0.3	2.4	16.2	3.0
fried in corn oil	100g	157	0.3	2.4	16.2	3.0
raw	100g	13	0.4	1.8	0.5	2.3
raw	1, average [10g]	1	trace	0.2	trace	0.2
Mustard and Cress						
raw	100g	13	0.4	1.6	0.6	3.3
raw	1 punnet [40g]	5	0.2	0.6	0.2	1.3
Okra						
boiled	100g	28	2.7	2.5	0.9	4.1
raw	100g	31	3.0	2.8	1.0	4.5
raw	10, medium [50g]	16	1.5	1.4	0.5	2.3
stir-fried in corn oil	100g	269	4.4	4.3	26.1	7.0
Onions						
boiled	100g	17	3.7	0.6	0.1	0.7
cocktail/ silverskin, drained	100g	15	3.1	0.6	0.1	0.6
fried in blended oil	100g	164	14.1	2.3	11.2	3.2
fried in corn oil	100g	164	14.1	2.3	11.2	3.2

Food Item	Amount	Kcals	Carb	Prot	Fat	Fibre
pickled, drained	100g	24	4.9	0.9	0.2	1.3
pickled, drained	1, average [10g]	2	0.5	0.1	trace	0.1
pickled, drained	1, large [25g]	6	1.2	0.2	trace	0.3
raw	100g	36	7.9	1.2	0.2	1.5
raw	1, average [90g]	32	7.1	1.1	0.2	1.4
raw	1 slice [20g]	7	1.6	0.2	trace	0.3
Parsnip						
boiled	100g	66	12.9	1.6	1.2	4.4
raw	100g	64	12.5	1.8	1.1	4.3
Peas						
boiled	100g	79	10.0	6.7	1.6	4.7
canned, re-heated, drained	100g	80	13.5	5.3	0.9	5.7
canned, re-heated, drained	1 tbsp [30g]	24	4.1	1.6	0.3	1.7
frozen, boiled	100g	69	9.7	6.0	0.9	7.3
Mange-tout, boiled	100g	26	3.3	3.2	0.1	4.0
Mange-tout, raw	100g	32	4.2	3.6	0.2	4.2
Mange-tout, stir-fried in blended oil	100g	71	3.5	3.8	4.8	4.4
mushy, canned, re-heated, drained	100g	81	13.8	5.8	0.7	1.8
mushy, canned, re-heated, drained	1 tbsp [30g]	24	4.1	1.7	0.2	0.5

Food Item	Amount	Kcals	Carb	Prot	Fat	Fibre
Petits pois, frozen, boiled	100g	49	5.5	5.0	0.9	6.4
processed, canned, re-heated, drained	100g	99	17.5	6.9	0.7	7.1
processed, canned, re-heated, drained	1 tbsp [30g]	30	5.3	2.1	0.2	2.1
raw	100g	83	11.3	6.9	1.5	4.7
Peppers						
Capsicum, green, boiled	100g	18	2.6	1.0	0.5	2.1
Capsicum, green, raw	100g	15	2.6	0.8	0.3	1.9
Capsicum, green, raw	1, medium [160g]	24	4.2	1.3	0.5	3.0
Capsicum, green, raw	1 sliced ring [10g]	2	0.3	0.1	trace	0.2
Capsicum, red, boiled	100g	34	7.0	1.1	0.4	2.1
Capsicum, red, raw	100g	32	6.4	1.0	0.4	1.9
Capsicum, red, raw	1, medium [160g]	51	10.2	1.6	0.6	3.0
Capsicum, red, raw	1 sliced ring [10g]	3	0.6	0.1	trace	0.2
mixed, raw	100g	20	0.7	2.9	0.6	1.9
Plantain						
boiled	100g	112	28.5	0.8	0.2	2.2
fried in vegetable oil	100g	267	47.5	1.5	9.2	4.0
raw	100g	117	29.4	1.1	0.3	2.3

Food Item	Amount	Kcals	Carb	Prot	Fat	Fibre
Potatoes (New)						
boiled	100g	75	17.8	1.5	0.3	1.2
boiled in skins	100g	66	15.4	1.4	0.3	1.3
canned, re-heated, drained	100g	63	15.1	1.5	0.1	2.3
raw	100g	70	16.1	1.7	0.3	1.3
Potatoes (Old)						
baked, flesh and skin	100g	136	31.7	3.9	0.2	2.7
baked, flesh and skin	1 medium-size [180g]	245	57.1	7.0	0.4	4.9
baked, flesh only	100g	77	18.0	2.2	0.1	1.7
baked, flesh only	1 medium-size [160g]	123	28.8	3.5	0.2	2.7
boiled	100g	72	17.0	1.8	0.1	1.2
boiled, mashed with butter	100g	104	15.5	1.8	4.3	1.3
boiled, mashed with margarine	100g	104	15.5	1.8	4.3	1.3
raw	100g	75	17.2	2.1	0.2	1.6
roast in blended oil	100g	149	25.9	2.9	4.5	2.4
roast in corn oil	100g	149	25.9	2.9	4.5	2.4

Food Item	Amount	Kcals	Carb	Prot	Fat	Fibre
roast in lard	100g	149	25.9	2.9	4.5	2.4
Potato croquettes						
fried in blended oil	100g	214	21.6	3.7	13.1	1.3
fried in blended oil	1, average [80g]	171	17.3	3.0	0.9	1.0
Potato waffles						
frozen, cooked	100g	84	30.3	3.2	8.2	2.3
Potatoes (Chips)						
fine cut, frozen, fried in blended oil	100g	364	41.2	4.5	21.3	4.0
fine cut, frozen, fried in corn oil	100g	364	41.2	4.5	21.3	4.0
homemade, fried in blended oil	100g	189	30.1	3.9	6.7	3.0
homemade, fried in corn oil	100g	189	30.1	3.9	6.7	3.0
oven, frozen, baked	100g	162	29.8	3.2	4.2	2.8
chip shop, fried in blended oil	100g	239	30.5	3.2	12.4	3.0
chip shop, fried in vegetable oil	100g	239	30.5	3.2	12.4	3.0

Food Item	Amount	Kcals	Carb	Prot	Fat	Fibre
chip shop, fried	1 average serving [200g]	478	61.0	6.4	24.8	6.0
straight cut, frozen, fried in blended oil	100g	273	36.0	4.1	13.5	3.5
straight cut, frozen, fried in corn oil	100g	273	36.0	4.1	13.5	3.5
french fries, retail [burger restaurants]	100g	280	34.0	3.3	15.5	3.1
french fries, retail [burger restaurants]	1 regular serving [150g]	420	51	5.0	23.3	4.7
Pumpkin						
raw	100g	13	2.2	0.7	0.2	0.5
boiled	100g	13	2.1	0.6	0.3	0.5
Quorn	100g	86	2.0	11.8	3.5	4.8
Radish						
raw	100g	12	1.9	0.7	0.2	0.9
raw	1, average [10g]	1	0.2	0.1	trace	0.1

Food Item	Amount	Kcals	Carb	Prot	Fat	Fibre
Ratatouille						
canned	100g	38	3.0	1.0	2.5	0.9
canned	400g can	150	12.0	4.0	10.0	3.6
Spinach						
boiled	100g	19	0.8	2.2	0.8	3.1
frozen, boiled	100g	21	0.5	3.1	0.8	3.1
raw	100g	25	1.6	2.8	0.8	3.9
Spring greens						
boiled	100g	20	1.6	1.9	0.7	3.4
raw	100g	33	3.1	3.0	1.0	6.1
Spring onions						
raw	100g	23	3.0	2.0	0.5	1.5
raw	1, average [20g]	5	0.6	0.4	0.1	0.3
Swede						
raw	100g	24	5.0	0.7	0.3	2.4
boiled	100g	11	2.3	0.3	0.1	1.2
Sweet potato						
boiled	100g	84	20.5	1.1	0.3	2.1

Food Item	Amount	Kcals	Carb	Prot	Fat	Fibre
raw	100g	87	21.3	1.2	0.3	2.3
Sweetcorn						
baby, canned, drained	100g	23	2.0	2.9	0.4	1.5
kernels, canned, drained	100g	122	26.6	2.9	1.2	3.9
kernels, canned, drained	1 tbsp [30g]	37	8.0	0.9	0.4	1.2
on-the-cob, whole, boiled	100g	66	11.6	2.5	1.4	2.5
on-the-cob, whole, boiled	1, kernels only [125g]	83	14.5	3.1	1.8	3.1
Tofu						
Soya bean, steamed	100g	73	0.7	8.1	4.2	0.3
Soya bean, steamed, fried	100g	261	2.0	23.5	17.7	0.9
Tomato-based product						
Passata	100g	29	6.0	1.1	0.2	N
Passata	550g jar	160	33.0	6.1	1.1	N
Tomato purée	100g	68	12.9	4.5	0.2	2.8
Tomatoes						
canned, with juice	100g	16	3.0	1.0	0.1	0.8
fried in blended oil	100g	91	5.0	0.7	7.7	2.8

Food Item	Amount	Kcals	Carb	Prot	Fat	Fibre
fried in corn oil	100g	91	5.0	0.7	7.7	2.8
grilled	100g	49	8.9	2.0	0.9	3.7
raw	100g	17	3.1	0.7	0.3	1.3
Turnip						
boiled	100g	12	2.0	0.6	0.2	2.0
raw	100g	23	4.7	0.9	0.3	2.5
Watercress						
raw	100g	22	0.4	3.0	1.0	3.0
raw	1 bunch [80g]	18	0.3	2.4	0.8	2.4
Yam						
boiled	100g	133	33.0	1.7	0.3	3.5
boiled	1, medium [130g]	173	42.9	2.2	0.4	4.6
raw	100g	114	28.2	1.5	0.3	3.7

Fruit

Food Item	Amount	Kcals	Carb	Prot	Fat	Fibre
Apples						
cooking, raw, peeled	100g	35	8.9	0.3	0.1	2.2
cooking, stewed with sugar	100g	74	19.1	0.3	0.1	1.8
cooking, stewed without sugar	100g	33	8.1	0.3	0.1	2.0
eating, raw, weighed without core	100g	47	11.8	0.4	0.1	2.0
eating, raw, with core	100g	42	10.5	0.4	0.1	1.8
eating, raw, with core	1 small [75g]	32	7.9	0.3	0.1	1.6
eating, raw, with core	1 medium [112g]	47	11.8	0.4	0.1	2.0
eating, raw, with core	1 large [170g]	71	17.9	0.7	0.2	3.0
eating, raw, peeled	100g	45	11.2	0.4	0.1	1.8
Apricots						
canned in juice	100g	34	8.4	0.5	0.1	1.2
canned in syrup	100g	63	16.1	0.4	0.1	1.2
raw, without stone	100g	31	8.5	0.3	0.1	1.9
raw, without stone	1 [65g]	20	5.5	0.2	0.1	1.2
semi-dried, ready-to-eat	100g	158	36.5	4.0	0.6	18.1

Food Item	Amount	Kcals	Carb	Prot	Fat	Fibre
Avocado						
raw, without skin or stone	100g	190	1.9	1.9	19.5	3.4
raw, without skin or stone	1 small [100g]	190	1.9	1.9	19.5	3.4
raw, without skin or stone	1 medium [145g]	275	2.8	2.8	28.3	4.9
raw, without skin or stone	1 large [195g]	371	3.7	3.7	38.0	6.6
Banana						
with skin	100g	95	23.2	1.2	0.3	3.0
with skin	1 small [130g]	123	30.2	1.6	0.4	3.9
with skin	1 medium [150g]	143	34.8	1.8	0.5	4.5
with skin	1 large [180g]	171	41.8	2.2	0.5	5.4
Blackberries						
raw	100g	25	5.1	0.9	0.2	6.6
stewed with sugar	100g	56	13.8	0.7	0.2	5.2
stewed without sugar	100g	21	4.4	0.8	0.2	5.6
Blackcurrants						
canned in juice	100g	31	7.6	0.8	trace	4.2
canned in syrup	100g	72	18.4	0.7	trace	3.6
raw	100g	28	6.6	0.9	trace	7.8
stewed with sugar	100g	58	15.0	0.7	trace	6.1

Food Item	Amount	Kcals	Carb	Prot	Fat	Fibre
Cherries						
canned in syrup	100g	71	18.5	0.5	trace	0.7
cherries, glacé	100g	251	66.4	0.4	trace	1.5
raw, without stone	100g	48	11.5	0.9	0.1	1.5
Clementines						
raw, without skin	100g	37	8.7	0.9	0.1	1.7
raw, without skin	1 small [40g]	15	3.5	0.4	trace	0.7
raw, without skin	1 medium [60g]	22	5.2	0.5	0.1	1.0
raw, without skin	1 large [80g]	30	7.0	0.7	0.1	1.4
Currants	100g	267	67.8	2.3	0.4	5.9
Damsons						
raw, without stones	100g	34	8.6	0.5	trace	3.3
raw, without stones	1 [15g]	5	1.3	trace	trace	0.5
stewed with sugar	100g	74	19.3	0.4	trace	3.0
Dates						
dried, with stones	100g	227	57.1	2.8	0.2	6.5
dried, with stone	1 [20g]	45	11.4	0.6	trace	1.3
raw, with stones	100g	107	26.9	1.3	0.1	3.1

Food Item	Amount	Kcals	Carb	Prot	Fat	Fibre
raw, with stone	1 [30g]	32	8.1	0.4	trace	0.9
Figs						
dried	100g	227	52.9	3.6	1.6	12.4
dried	1 [20g]	45	10.6	0.7	0.3	2.5
semi-dried, ready-to-eat	100g	209	48.6	3.3	1.5	11.4
semi-dried, ready-to-eat	1 [35g]	73	17.0	1.2	0.5	4.0
Fruit cocktail						
canned in juice	100g	29	7.2	0.4	trace	1.0
canned in syrup	100g	57	14.8	0.4	trace	1.0
Fruit pie filling						
average	100g	77	20.1	0.4	trace	1.6
Fruit salad						
home made [bananas, oranges, apples, pears and grapes]	100g	55	13.8	0.7	0.1	1.5
Gooseberries						
cooking, raw	100g	19	3.0	1.1	0.4	2.9
dessert, canned in syrup	100g	73	18.5	0.4	0.2	1.7
stewed with sugar	100g	54	12.9	0.7	0.3	2.3

167

Food Item	Amount	Kcals	Carb	Prot	Fat	Fibre
stewed without sugar	100g	16	2.5	0.9	0.3	2.4
Grapefruit						
canned in juice	100g	30	7.3	0.6	trace	0.8
canned in syrup	100g	60	15.5	0.5	trace	0.9
raw, with skin	100g	20	4.6	0.5	0.1	1.1
raw, with skin	1 small [250g]	50	11.5	1.3	0.3	2.8
raw, with skin	1 medium [340g]	68	15.6	1.7	0.3	3.7
raw, with skin	1 large [425g]	85	19.6	2.1	0.4	4.7
Grapes						
raw, black and white	100g	60	15.4	0.4	0.1	0.8
raw, black and white	1 [5g]	3	0.8	trace	trace	trace
Guava						
canned in syrup	100g	60	15.7	0.4	trace	3.2
raw	100g	26	5.0	0.8	0.5	4.7
Kiwi fruit						
raw, without skin	100g	49	10.6	1.1	0.5	1.9
raw, without skin	1 [60g]	29	6.3	0.7	0.3	1.1

Food Item	Amount	Kcals	Carb	Prot	Fat	Fibre
Lemons						
raw, with peel	100g	19	3.2	1.0	0.3	4.7
raw, with peel	1 medium [125g]	24	4.0	1.3	0.3	5.9
Lychees						
canned in syrup	100g	68	17.7	0.4	trace	0.7
raw, without stone	100g	58	14.3	0.9	0.1	1.5
raw, without stone	1 [15g]	9	2.1	0.1	trace	0.2
Mandarin oranges						
canned in juice	100g	32	7.7	0.7	trace	0.3
canned in syrup	100g	52	13.4	0.5	trace	0.3
Mangoes						
canned in syrup	100g	77	20.3	0.3	trace	0.9
raw, without stone or skin	100g	57	14.1	0.7	0.2	2.9
raw, without stone or skin	1 slice [40g]	23	5.6	0.3	trace	1.2
Melon						
Canteloupe, without skin or seeds	100g	19	4.2	0.6	0.1	0.9

Food Item	Amount	Kcals	Carb	Prot	Fat	Fibre
Canteloupe, without skin or seeds	1 slice [150g]	29	6.3	0.9	0.2	1.3
Galia, without skin or seeds	100g	24	5.6	0.5	0.1	0.9
Galia, without skin or seeds	1 slice [150g]	36	8.4	0.8	0.2	1.3
Honeydew, without skin or seeds	100g	28	6.6	0.6	0.1	0.8
Honeydew, without skin or seeds	1 slice [180g]	50	11.8	1.1	0.2	1.4
Watermelon, without skin or seeds	100g	31	7.1	0.5	0.3	0.3
Watermelon, without skin or seeds	1 slice [200g]	62	14.2	1.0	0.6	0.6
Mixed fruit						
dried	100g	268	68.1	2.3	0.4	6.4
dried	1 heaped tbsp [25g]	67	17.0	0.6	0.1	0.6
Nectarines						
raw, without stones	100g	40	9.0	1.4	0.1	2.2
raw, without stone	1 small [125g]	50	11.3	1.8	0.1	2.8
raw, without stone	1 medium [140g]	56	12.6	2.0	0.1	3.1

Food Item	Amount	Kcals	Carb	Prot	Fat	Fibre
raw, without stone	1 large [175g]	70	15.8	3.5	0.2	3.9
Olives						
in brine, without stones	100g	103	trace	0.9	11.0	4.0
Oranges						
raw, without skin	100g	37	8.5	1.1	0.1	1.8
raw, without skin	1 small [120g]	46	10.6	1.4	0.1	2.4
raw, without skin	1 medium [160g]	59	13.6	2.2	0.2	2.9
raw, without skin	1 large [210g]	78	17.9	2.3	2.2	3.8
Passion fruit						
raw, without skin	100g	36	5.8	2.6	0.4	3.3
raw, without skin	1 [15g]	5	0.9	0.4	trace	0.5
Paw-paw						
raw	100g	36	8.8	0.5	0.1	2.3
Peaches						
canned in juice	100g	39	9.7	0.6	trace	0.9
canned in syrup	100g	55	14.0	0.5	trace	0.9
raw, without stone	100g	33	7.6	1.0	0.1	2.3

Food Item	Amount	Kcals	Carb	Prot	Fat	Fibre
raw, without stone	1 small [70g]	23	5.3	0.7	trace	1.6
raw, without stone	1 medium [110g]	36	8.4	1.1	0.1	2.5
raw, without stone	1 large [150g]	50	11.4	1.5	0.2	3.4
Pears						
canned in juice	100g	33	8.5	0.3	trace	1.5
canned in syrup	100g	50	13.2	0.2	trace	1.5
raw, without core	100g	40	10.0	0.3	0.1	2.2
raw, without core	1 medium [200g]	80	20.0	0.6	0.2	4.4
raw, peeled	100g	41	10.4	0.3	0.1	2.7
Peel						
mixed, dried	100g	231	59.1	0.3	0.9	4.8
Pineapple						
canned in juice	100g	47	12.2	0.3	trace	0.8
canned in syrup	100g	64	16.5	0.5	trace	0.8
raw, without skin	100g	41	10.1	0.4	0.2	1.3
raw, without skin	1 slice [80g]	33	8.1	0.3	0.2	1.0
Plums						
canned in syrup	100g	59	15.5	0.3	trace	1.0

Food Item	Amount	Kcals	Carb	Prot	Fat	Fibre
raw, without stone	100g	34	8.3	0.5	0.1	2.3
raw, without stone	1 small [30g]	10	2.5	0.2	trace	0.7
raw, without stone	1 medium [55g]	19	4.6	0.3	0.1	1.3
raw, without stone	1 large [85g]	29	7.1	0.4	0.1	2.0
stewed with sugar, weighed with stones	100g	75	19.2	0.5	0.1	1.8
stewed without sugar, weighed with stones	100g	29	6.9	0.4	0.1	1.8
Prunes						
canned in juice	100g	79	19.7	0.7	0.2	2.4
canned in syrup	100g	90	23.0	0.6	0.2	2.8
semi-dried, ready-to-eat	100g	141	34.0	2.5	0.4	12.8
semi-dried, ready-to-eat	1 [15g]	21	5.1	0.4	trace	1.9
Raisins	100g	272	69.3	2.1	0.4	6.9
	1 tbsp [30g]	82	20.8	0.6	trace	1.8
Raspberries						
canned in syrup	100g	88	22.5	0.6	0.1	4.5
raw	100g	25	4.6	1.4	0.3	6.7

173

Food Item	Amount	Kcals	Carb	Prot	Fat	Fibre
Rhubarb						
canned in syrup	100g	65	16.9	0.5	trace	1.3
raw	100g	7	0.8	0.9	0.1	2.3
stewed with sugar	100g	48	11.5	0.9	0.1	2.0
stewed without sugar	100g	7	0.7	0.9	0.1	2.1
Satsumas						
raw, without peel	100g	36	8.5	0.9	0.1	1.7
raw, without peel	1 small [50g]	18	4.3	0.5	0.1	0.9
raw, without peel	1 medium [70g]	25	6.0	0.6	0.1	1.2
raw, without peel	1 large [90g]	32	7.7	0.8	0.1	1.5
Strawberries						
canned in syrup	100g	65	16.9	0.5	trace	0.9
raw	100g	27	6.0	0.8	0.1	2.0
raw	1 [12g]	3	6.1	0.1	trace	0.2
Sultanas						
	100g	275	69.4	2.7	0.4	6.3
	1 tbsp [30g]	83	20.8	0.8	trace	1.9
Tangerines						
raw	100g	35	8.0	0.9	0.1	1.7
raw	1 small [50g]	18	4.0	0.5	0.1	0.9

Food Item	Amount	Kcals	Carb	Prot	Fat	Fibre
raw	1 medium [70g]	25	5.6	0.6	0.1	1.2
raw	1 large [90g]	32	7.2	0.6	0.1	1.5

Fish

Food Item	Amount	Kcals	Carb	Prot	Fat	Fibre
Anchovies						
canned in oil, drained	100g	280	0	25.2	19.9	0
canned in oil, drained	1 anchovy [3g]	8	0	0.8	0.6	0
Cockles						
boiled	100g	48	trace	11.3	0.3	0
boiled	1 cockle [4g]	2	0	0.5	trace	0
Cod						
dried, salted, boiled	100g	138	0	32.5	0.9	0
Fillets, baked, with butter added	100g	96	0	21.4	1.2	0
Fillets, poached in milk with butter added	100g	94	0	20.9	1.1	0
Fillets, raw	100g	76	0	17.4	0.7	0
in batter, fried in blended oil	100g	199	7.5	19.6	10.3	0.3
Steaks, frozen, raw	100g	68	0	15.6	0.6	0

Food Item	Amount	Kcals	Carb	Prot	Fat	Fibre
Crab						
boiled	100g	127	0	20.1	5.2	0
canned	100g	81	0	18.1	0.9	0
Dogfish						
in batter, fried in blended oil	100g	265	7.7	16.7	18.8	0.3
Fish fingers						
fried in blended oil	100g	233	17.2	13.5	12.7	0.6
fried in oil or lard	1 fish finger [28g]	65	4.8	3.8	3.6	0.2
grilled	100g	214	19.3	15.1	9.0	0.7
grilled	1 fish finger [28g]	60	5.4	4.3	2.5	0.2
Fish-based dishes						
Fish pie, home-made	100g	105	12.3	8.0	3.0	0.9
Kedgeree, home-made	100g	166	10.5	14.2	7.9	0.3
Fish-based products						
Fish cakes, fried	100g	188	15.1	9.1	10.5	0.6
Fish cakes, fried	1 fish cake [50g]	94	7.6	4.6	5.3	0.3
Fish paste	100g	169	3.7	15.3	10.4	0.2
Taramasalata	100g	446	4.1	3.2	46.4	0.6

Food Item	Amount	Kcals	Carb	Prot	Fat	Fibre
Taramasalata	1 tbsp [45g]	201	1.8	1.4	20.9	0.3
Haddock						
fillet, raw	100g	73	0	16.8	0.6	0
in breadcrumbs, fried in blended oil	100g	174	3.6	21.4	8.3	0.2
in breadcrumbs, fried in dripping	100g	174	3.6	21.4	8.3	0.2
middle cut, steamed	100g	98	0	22.8	0.8	0
middle cut, steamed	85g portion	83	0	19.4	0.7	0
smoked, steamed	100g	101	0	23.3	0.9	0
smoked, steamed	85g portion	86	5.2	19.8	0.8	0
middle cut, steamed	100g	98	0	22.8	0.8	0
Halibut						
middle cut, steamed	100g	83	0	19.4	0.7	0
raw	100g	92	0	17.7	2.4	0
Herring						
fried in oatmeal	100g	234	1.5	23.1	15.1	1.3
grilled	100g	135	0	13.9	8.8	0
raw	100g	234	0	16.8	18.5	0

Food Item	Amount	Kcals	Carb	Prot	Fat	Fibre
Kipper						
baked	100g	205	0	25.5	11.4	0
Lemon sole						
in breadcrumbs, fried	100g	216	9.3	16.1	13.0	0.4
raw	100g	81	0	17.1	1.4	0
steamed	100g	91	0	20.6	0.9	0
Lobster						
boiled	100g	119	0	22.1	3.4	0
Mackerel						
fried	100g	188	0	21.5	11.3	0
raw	100g	223	0	19.0	16.3	0
smoked	100g	354	0	18.9	30.9	0
Mussels						
boiled	100g	87	trace	17.2	2.0	0
boiled	1 mussel [7g]	6.1	trace	1.2	0.1	0
Moules mariniere	100g	143	4.6	6.5	11.3	0.4
Pilchards						
in tomato sauce, canned	100g	126	0.7	18.8	5.4	trace

179

Food Item	Amount	Kcals	Carb	Prot	Fat	Fibre
in tomato sauce, canned	1 pilchard [55g]	69.3	0.4	10.3	3.0	trace
Plaice						
in batter, fried in blended oil	100g	279	14.4	15.8	18.0	0
in bread-crumbs, fried	100g	228	8.6	18.0	13.7	0.4
raw	100g	91	0	17.9	2.2	0
steamed	100g	93	0	18.9	1.9	0
Prawns						
boiled	100g	107	0	22.6	1.8	0
boiled	1 prawn [3g]	3	0	0.7	0.1	0
boiled	portion for prawn cocktail [40g]	43	0	9.0	0.8	0
Roe						
Cod, hard, in breadcrumbs, fried	100g	202	3.0	20.9	11.9	0.1
Herring, soft, rolled in flour, fried	100g	244	4.7	21.1	15.8	0.1
Saithe						
raw	100g	73	0	17.0	0.5	0

Food Item	Amount	Kcals	Carb	Prot	Fat	Fibre
steamed	100g	99	0	23.3	0.6	0
Salmon						
canned	100g	155	0	20.3	8.2	0
raw	100g	182	0	18.4	12.0	0
smoked	100g	142	0	25.4	4.5	0
steamed	100g	197	0	20.1	13.0	0
Sardines						
in oil, canned, drained	100g	217	0	23.7	13.6	0
in oil, canned, drained	1 sardine [25g]	54.3	0	5.9	3.4	0
in tomato sauce, canned	100g	177	0.5	17.8	11.6	trace
Scampi						
in breadcrumbs, fried	100g	316	28.9	12.2	17.6	1.1
in breadcrumbs, fried	1 piece [15g]	79	7.2	3.1	4.4	0.2
Shrimps						
canned, drained	100g	94	0	20.8	1.2	0
frozen	100g	73	0	16.5	0.8	0
Skate						
in batter, fried	100g	199	4.9	17.9	12.1	0.2

Food Item	Amount	Kcals	Carb	Prot	Fat	Fibre
Squid						
frozen, raw	100g	66	0	13.1	1.5	0
Trout						
Brown, steamed	100g	135	0	23.5	4.5	0
Tuna						
in brine, canned, drained	100g	99	0	23.5	0.6	0
in oil, canned, drained	100g	189	0	27.1	9.0	0
Whelks						
boiled, weighed with shell	100g	14	trace	2.8	0.3	0
Whitebait						
rolled in flour, fried	100g	525	5.3	19.5	47.5	0.2
rolled in flour, fried	1 whole	21	0.2	0.8	1.9	trace
Whiting						
in breadcrumbs, fried	100g	191	7.0	18.1	10.3	0.2
in breadcrumbs, fried	180g portion	344	12.6	32.6	18.5	0.4
steamed	100g	92	0	20.9	0.9	0
steamed	85g portion	78	0	17.8	0.8	0
Winkles						
boiled, weighed with shell	100g	14	trace	2.9	0.3	0

Egg and Egg-based Dishes

Food Item	Amount	Kcals	Carb	Prot	Fat	Fibre
Chicken egg						
boiled	100g	147	trace	12.5	10.8	0
boiled	1, size 1 [67g]	98	trace	8.4	7.2	0
boiled	1, size 2 [61g]	90	trace	7.6	6.6	0
boiled	1, size 3 [57g]	84	trace	7.1	6.2	0
boiled	1, size 4 [47g]	69	trace	5.9	5.1	0
fried in vegetable oil	100g	179	trace	13.6	13.9	0
fried in vegetable oil	1, average [60g]	107	trace	8.2	8.3	0
poached	100g	147	trace	12.5	10.8	0
poached	1, average [50g]	74	trace	6.3	5.4	0
scrambled, with milk	100g	247	0.6	10.7	22.6	0
white, raw	100g	36	trace	9.0	trace	0
whole, raw	100g	147	trace	12.5	10.8	0
whole, raw	1, size 1 [67g]	98	trace	8.4	7.2	0
whole, raw	1, size 2 [61g]	90	trace	7.6	6.6	0
whole, raw	1, size 3 [57g]	84	trace	7.1	6.2	0

Food Item	Amount	Kcals	Carb	Prot	Fat	Fibre
whole, raw	1, size 4 [47g]	69	trace	5.9	5.1	0
yolk, raw	100g	339	trace	16.1	30.5	0
Duck egg						
whole, raw	100g	163	trace	14.3	11.8	0
whole, raw	1, average [75g]	122	trace	17.2	14.2	0
Egg-based dessert						
Meringue, with cream	100g	376	40.0	3.3	23.6	0
Meringue, with cream	1 [28g]	105	11.2	0.9	6.6	0
Meringue, without cream	100g	379	95.4	5.3	trace	0
Meringue, without cream	1 [8g]	30	7.6	0.4	trace	0
Egg-based dish						
Egg-fried rice	100g	208	25.7	4.2	10.6	0.4
Egg-fried rice	300g portion	624	77.1	12.6	31.8	1.2
Omelette, cheese	100g	266	trace	15.9	22.6	0
Omelette, cheese	2 eggs [180g]	479	trace	28.6	40.7	0
Omelette, plain	100g	191	trace	10.9	16.4	0
Omelette, plain	2 eggs [120g]	229	trace	13.1	19.7	0
Quiche, cheese and egg	100g	314	17.3	12.5	22.2	0.7
Quiche, cheese and egg,						

Food Item	Amount	Kcals	Carb	Prot	Fat	Fibre
wholemeal	100g	308	14.5	13.2	22.4	1.8
Quiche, cheese and egg,						
wholemeal	190g slice	585	27.6	25.1	42.6	3.4
Scotch egg	100g	251	13.1	12.0	17.1	1.6
Scotch egg	1, average [120g]	301	15.7	14.4	20.5	1.9

Milk and Dairy Products

Food Item	Amount	Kcals	Carb	Prot	Fat	Fibre
Butter	100g	737	trace	0.5	81.7	0
thin spreading for bread	[7g]	52	trace	trace	2.9	0
thick spreading for bread	[12g]	88	trace	0.1	9.8	0
average restaurant portion	[20g]	147	trace	0.1	16.3	0
Cheese						
Brie	100g	319	trace	19.3	26.9	0
Camembert	100g	297	trace	20.9	23.7	0
Cheddar, average	100g	412	0.1	25.5	34.4	0
Cheddar, vegetarian	100g	425	trace	25.8	35.7	0
Cheddar-type, reduced fat	100g	261	trace	31.5	15.0	0
Cheese spread	100g	276	4.4	13.5	22.8	0
Cottage cheese, plain	100g	98	2.1	13.8	3.9	0
Cottage cheese, plain	112g pot	110	2.4	2.0	4.4	0
Cottage cheese, reduced fat	100g	78	3.3	13.3	1.4	0
Cottage cheese, reduced fat	112g pot	87	3.7	1.5	1.6	0

Food Item	Amount	Kcals	Carb	Prot	Fat	Fibre
Cottage cheese, with additions	100g	95	2.6	12.8	3.8	trace
Cottage cheese, with additions	112g pot	106	2.9	14.3	4.3	trace
Cream cheese	100g	439	trace	3.1	47.4	0
Danish Blue	100g	347	trace	20.1	29.6	0
Dolcellate	100g	320	0.2	19.2	27	0
Edam	100g	333	trace	26.0	25.4	0
Emmental	100g	401	trace	29	31.4	trace
Feta	100g	250	1.5	15.6	20.2	0
Fromage Frais, fruit	100g	131	13.8	6.8	5.8	trace
Fromage Frais, fruit	60g pot	79	8.3	4.1	3.5	trace
Fromage Frais, plain	100g	113	5.7	6.8	7.1	0
Fromage Frais, plain	60g pot	68	3.4	4.1	4.3	0
Fromage Frais, very low fat	100g	58	6.8	7.7	0.2	trace
Fromage Frais, very low fat	60g pot	35	4.1	4.6	0.1	trace
Gouda	100g	375	trace	24.0	31.0	0
Hard cheese, average	100g	405	0.1	24.7	34.0	0
Parmesan	100g	452	trace	39.4	32.7	0
Processed, plain	100g	330	0.9	20.8	27.0	0
Soft cheese, full fat	100g	313	trace	8.6	31.0	0

Food Item	Amount	Kcals	Carb	Prot	Fat	Fibre
Soft cheese, medium fat	100g	179	3.1	9.2	14.5	0
Stilton	100g	411	0.1	22.7	35.5	0
White, average	100g	376	0.1	23.4	31.3	0
Cream, fresh						
clotted	100g	586	2.3	1.6	63.5	0
clotted	carton [150g]	879	3.5	2.4	95.3	0
double	100g	449	2.7	1.7	48.0	0
double	carton [150g]	674	4.1	2.6	72.0	0
half	100g	148	4.3	3.0	13.3	0
half	carton [150g]	222	6.5	4.5	20.0	0
single	100g	198	4.1	2.6	19.1	0
single	carton [150g]	297	6.2	3.9	28.7	0
soured	100g	205	3.8	2.9	19.9	0
soured	carton [150g]	308	5.7	4.4	30.0	0
whipping	100g	373	3.1	2.0	39.3	0
whipping	carton [150g]	560	4.7	3.0	59.0	0
Cream, sterilised						
canned	100g	239	3.7	2.5	23.9	0

188

Food Item	Amount	Kcals	Carb	Prot	Fat	Fibre
Cream, UHT						
canned spray	100g	309	3.5	1.9	32.0	0
Dairy/Fat spread	100g	662	trace	0.4	73.4	0
	medium spreading for bread [10g]	66	trace	trace	7.3	0
Dessert						
Cheesecake	100g	242	33.0	5.7	10.6	0.9
Custard, made with skimmed milk	100g	79	16.8	3.8	0.1	trace
Custard, made with whole milk	100g	117	16.6	3.7	4.5	trace
Milk pudding, made with skimmed milk	100g	93	20.1	4.0	0.2	0.2
Milk pudding, made with whole milk	100g	129	19.9	3.9	4.3	0.2
Mousse, chocolate	100g	139	19.9	4.0	5.4	N
Mousse, fruit	100g	137	18.0	4.5	5.7	N
Rice pudding, canned	100g	89	14.0	3.4	2.5	0.2
Trifle, home-made	100g	160	22.3	3.6	6.3	0.5

Food Item	Amount	Kcals	Carb	Prot	Fat	Fibre
Trifle, home-made, with fresh cream	100g	166	19.5	2.4	9.2	0.5
Ice cream						
Choc ice	50g bar	139	14.1	1.8	8.8	trace
Cornetto	75g cone	195	25.9	2.8	9.6	trace
Dairy, flavoured	100g	179	24.7	3.5	8.0	trace
Dairy, vanilla	100g	194	24.4	3.6	9.8	trace
Luxury, full cream, vanilla	100g	237	17.4	4.4	16.6	trace
Lemon sorbet	100g	131	34.2	0.9	trace	0
Non-dairy, flavoured	100g	166	23.2	3.1	7.4	trace
Non-dairy, vanilla	100g	178	23.1	3.2	8.7	trace
Ice cream dessert						
Arctic roll	100g	200	33.3	4.1	6.6	0.8
Chocolate nut sundae	100g	278	34.2	3.0	15.3	0.2
Milk, condensed						
skimmed, sweetened	100g	267	60.0	10.0	0.2	0
whole, sweetened	100g	333	55.5	8.5	10.1	0
Milk, dried						
skimmed	100g	348	52.9	36.1	0.6	0

Food Item	Amount	Kcals	Carb	Prot	Fat	Fibre
skimmed, with vegetable fat	100g	487	42.6	23.3	25.9	0
Milk, evaporated						
whole	100g	151	8.5	8.4	9.4	0
whole	170g can	257	14.5	14.3	16.0	0
Milk, flavoured						
mixed flavours, skimmed	100g	68	10.6	3.6	1.5	0
mixed flavours, skimmed	½ pint [293g]	199	31.1	10.6	4.4	0
Milk, goat's						
pasteurised	100g	60	4.4	3.1	3.5	0
pasteurised	1 pint [585g]	351	25.7	18.1	20.5	0
Milk, semi-skimmed						
pasteurised	100g	46	5.0	3.3	1.6	0
pasteurised	1 pint [585g]	269	29.3	19.3	9.4	0
pasteurised	30g portion for tea/coffee	14	1.5	1.0	0.5	0
fortified plus smp	100g	51	5.8	3.7	1.6	0
fortified plus smp	1 pint [585g]	2988	33.9	21.6	9.4	0
UHT	100g	46	4.8	3.3	1.7	0
UHT	1 pint [585g]	269	28.1	19.3	9.9	0

Food Item	Amount	Kcals	Carb	Prot	Fat	Fibre
Milk, sheep's						
raw	100g	95	5.1	5.4	6.0	0
raw	1 pint [585g]	556	29.8	31.6	35.1	0
pasteurised	100g	33	5.0	3.3	0.1	0
pasteurised	1 pint [585g]	193	29.3	19.3	0	0
Milk, skimmed						
pasteurised	30g portion for tea					
	or coffee	10	1.5	1.0	trace	0
fortified plus smp	100g	39	6.0	3.8	0.1	0
fortified plus smp	1 pint [585g]	228	35.1	22.2	0.6	0
UHT, fortified	100g	35	5.0	3.5	0.2	0
Milk, soya						
plain	100g	32	0.8	2.9	1.9	0
plain	1 pint [585g]	187	4.7	17.0	11.1	0
flavoured	100g	40	3.6	2.8	1.7	0
flavoured	1 pint [585g]	232	21.1	16.4	9.0	0
Milk, whole						
pasteurised	100g	66	4.8	3.2	3.9	0
pasteurised	1 pint [585g]	386	28.1	18.7	22.8	0

Food Item	Amount	Kcals	Carb	Prot	Fat	Fibre
pasteurised	30g portion for tea or coffee	20	1.4	1.0	1.2	0
sterilised	100g	66	4.5	3.5	3.9	0
sterilised	1 pint [585g]	386	26.3	20.5	22.8	0
UHT, fortified	1 pint [585g]	205	29.3	20.5	1.2	0
Yoghurt						
drinking	100g	62	13.1	3.1	trace	trace
Greek, cows	100g	115	2.0	6.4	9.1	0
Greek, sheep's	100g	106	5.6	4.4	7.5	0
Low calorie	100g	41	6.0	4.3	0.2	0
Low fat, flavoured	100g	90	17.9	3.8	0.9	0
Low fat, fruit	100g	90	17.9	4.1	0.7	trace
Low fat, plain	100g	56	7.5	5.1	0.8	0
Soya	100g	72	3.9	5.0	4.2	0
Whole milk, fruit	100g	105	15.7	5.1	2.8	trace
Whole milk, plain	100g	79	7.8	5.7	3.0	0
Whole milk, plain	150g carton	119	11.7	8.6	4.5	0
Yoghurt-based dish						
Tzatziki	100g	66	2.0	3.7	4.9	0.2

193

Savoury Dishes

Food Item	Amount	Kcals	Carb	Prot	Fat	Fibre
Cereal-based dishes						
Pizza, cheese and tomato, home-made	100g	235	24.8	9.0	11.8	1.8
Cereal/Vegetable dishes						
Pancake roll, with vegetable and beansprout filling	100g	217	20.9	6.6	12.5	N
Egg-based dishes						
Omelette, cheese	100g	266	trace	15.9	22.6	0
Omelette, cheese	2 eggs [180g]	479	trace	28.6	40.7	0
Omelette, plain	100g	191	trace	10.9	16.4	0
Omelette, plain	2 eggs [120g]	229	trace	13.1	19.7	0
Quiche, cheese and egg	100g	314	17.3	12.5	22.2	0.7
Quiche, cheese & egg, wholemeal	100g	308	14.5	13.2	22.4	1.8
Fish-based dishes						
Cod fried in batter [chip shop]	100g	199	7.5	19.6	10.3	0.3

Food Item	Amount	Kcals	Carb	Prot	Fat	Fibre
Dogfish in batter	100g	265	7.7	16.7	18.8	0.3
Fish cakes, fried	100g	188	15.1	9.1	10.5	0.6
Fish cakes, fried	1 fish cake [50g]	94	7.6	4.6	5.3	0.3
Fish fingers, fried	100g	233	17.2	13.5	12.7	0.6
Fish fingers, fried	1 fish finger [28g]	65	4.8	3.8	3.6	0.2
Fish fingers, grilled	100g	214	19.3	15.1	9.0	0.7
Fish fingers, grilled	1 fish finger, [28g]	60	5.4	4.3	2.5	0.2
Fish pie, home-made	100g	105	12.3	8.0	3.0	0.9
Haddock fried in breadcrumbs	100g	174	3.6	21.4	8.3	0.2
Plaice fried in batter [chip shop]	100g	279	14.4	15.8	18.0	0.5
Scampi, fried in breadcrumbs	100g	316	28.9	12.2	17.6	1.1
Fish/Rice dish						
Kedgeree, home-made	100g	166	10.5	14.2	7.9	0.3
Meat-based dishes						
Beef chow mein	100g	136	14.7	6.7	6.0	2.0
Beef curry	100g	137	6.3	13.5	6.6	1.2
Beef curry with rice	100g	137	16.9	8.8	4.3	0.7
Beef kheema	100g	413	0.3	18.2	37.7	0.2

Food Item	Amount	Kcals	Carb	Prot	Fat	Fibre
Beef koftas	100g	353	3.4	23.3	27.6	0.7
Beef steak pudding	100g	224	18.8	10.8	12.3	1.0
Beef stew	100g	120	4.6	9.7	7.2	0.7
Beefburger, fried, in burger bun	105g beefburger, 50g bun	410	31.8	26.0	20.7	3.2
Beefburger, fried, in burger bun, with french fries	105g beefburger, 50g bun, 93g fries	670	63.4	29.1	35.1	6.1
Bolognese sauce	100g	145	3.7	8.0	11.1	1.1
Chicken curry	100g	205	3.1	10.2	17.0	1.0
Chicken curry with rice	100g	144	16.9	7.8	5.5	0.8
Chicken in white sauce, canned	100g	186	3.5	9.5	15.0	0.5
Chilli con carne	100g	151	8.3	11.0	8.5	3.2
Cottage pie, frozen	100g	110	11.4	5.1	4.7	0.6
Curried meat	100g	162	9.1	8.5	10.5	1.8
Hot pot, home-made	100g	144	10.1	9.4	4.5	1.4
Irish stew	100g	123	9.1	5.3	7.6	1.0
Lamb hot pot, frozen	100g	92	7.9	7.9	3.4	1.2

Food Item	Amount	Kcals	Carb	Prot	Fat	Fibre
Lamb kheema	100g	328	2.3	14.6	29.1	0.6
Lasagne	100g	102	12.8	5.0	3.8	0.5
Moussaka, frozen	100g	105	9.9	7.0	4.4	0.6
Moussaka, home-made	100g	184	7.0	9.1	13.6	1.0
Mutton biriani	100g	276	25.1	7.5	16.9	1.4
Mutton curry	100g	374	3.9	14.9	33.4	1.0
Shepherd's pie	100g	118	8.2	8.0	6.2	0.7
Spaghetti bolognese	450g portion [220g sauce, 230g pasta]	558	59.2	25.9	26.0	6.5
Steak and kidney pie	100g	323	25.6	9.1	21.2	1.0
Steak and kidney pie	1 pie [200g]	646	51.2	18.2	42.4	2.0
Steak and kidney pie, pastry top	100g	286	15.9	15.2	18.4	0.7
Pasta dishes						
Macaroni cheese with ham, frozen	100g	146	13.3	9.9	5.7	0.5
Macaroni cheese, home-made	100g	178	13.6	7.3	10.8	0.8
Rice-based dishes						
Egg-fried rice	100g	208	25.7	4.2	10.6	0.9
Risotto, plain	100g	224	34.4	3.0	9.3	1.3

Food Item	Amount	Kcals	Carb	Prot	Fat	Fibre
Risotto, plain	300g portion	672	103.2	9.0	27.9	3.9
Vegetable dish						
Cauliflower cheese	100g	105	5.1	5.9	6.9	1.4
Vegetable-based dishes						
Ratatouille, canned	100g	38	3.0	1.0	2.5	0.9
Mixed vegetable chilli, canned	100g	86	9.1	4.3	3.8	N

Meat and Meat Products

Food Item	Amount	Kcals	Carb	Prot	Fat	Fibre
Bacon						
Collar joint, boiled	100g	325	0	20.4	27.0	0
Collar joint, raw	100g	319	0	14.6	28.9	0
Gammon joint, boiled	100g	269	0	24.7	18.9	0
Gammon joint, raw	100g	236	0	17.6	18.3	0
Gammon rasher, grilled	100g	228	0	29.5	12.2	0
Rasher [back], grilled	100g	405	0	25.3	33.8	0
Rasher [back], grilled	1 rasher [25g]	101	0	6.3	8.5	0
Rasher [back], raw	100g	428	0	14.2	41.2	0
Rasher [middle], grilled	100g	416	0	24.9	35.1	0
Rasher [middle], grilled	1 rasher [40g]	166	0	10.0	14.0	0
Rasher [middle], raw	100g	425	0	14.3	40.9	0
Rasher [streaky], grilled	100g	422	0	24.5	36.0	0
Rasher [streaky], grilled	1 rasher [20g]	84	0	4.9	7.2	0
Rasher [streaky], raw	100g	414	0	14.6	39.5	0

Food Item	Amount	Kcals	Carb	Prot	Fat	Fibre
Beef						
Brisket, boiled	100g	326	0	27.6	23.9	0
Brisket, raw	100g	252	0	16.8	20.5	0
Forerib, raw	100g	290	0	16.0	25.1	0
Forerib, roast	100g	349	0	22.4	28.8	0
Mince, raw	100g	221	0	18.8	16.2	0
Mince, stewed	100g	229	0	23.1	15.2	0
Rump steak, fried	100g	246	0	28.6	14.6	0
Rump steak, grilled	100g	218	0	27.3	12.1	0
Rump steak, raw	100g	197	0	18.9	13.5	0
Salted	100g	119	0	27.1	0.4	0
Silverside, salted, boiled	100g	242	0	28.6	14.2	0
Sirloin, raw	100g	272	0	16.6	22.8	0
Sirloin, roast	100g	284	0	23.6	21.1	0
Stewing steak, raw	100g	176	0	20.2	10.6	0
Stewing steak, stewed	100g	223	0	30.9	11.0	0
Topside, raw	100g	179	0	19.6	11.2	0
Topside, roast	100g	214	0	26.6	12.0	0

Food Item	Amount	Kcals	Carb	Prot	Fat	Fibre
Beef-based dishes						
Beef kheema	100g	413	0.3	18.2	37.7	0.2
Beef steak pudding	100g	224	18.8	10.8	12.3	1.0
Beef stew, home made	100g	120	4.6	9.7	7.2	0.7
Bolognese sauce	100g	145	3.7	8.0	11.1	1.1
Chilli con carne	100g	151	8.3	11.0	8.5	3.2
Chow mein	100g	136	14.7	6.7	6.0	2.0
Curry	100g	137	6.3	13.5	6.6	1.2
Curry with rice	100g	137	16.9	8.8	4.3	0.7
Stewed steak, canned, with gravy	100g	176	1.0	14.8	12.5	0
Beefburgers, frozen, raw	100g	265	5.3	15.2	20.5	1.3
Beefburgers, frozen, fried	100g	264	7.0	20.4	17.3	1.3
Beefburgers, frozen, fried	1 burger [50g]	132	3.5	10.2	8.7	0.7
Corned beef, canned	100g	217	0	26.9	12.1	0
Chicken						
Breaded, fried in oil	100g	242	14.8	18.0	12.7	0.7
Dark meat, boiled	100g	204	0	28.6	9.9	0
Dark meat, raw	100g	126	0	19.1	5.5	0

Food Item	Amount	Kcals	Carb	Prot	Fat	Fibre
Dark meat, roast	100g	155	0	23.1	6.9	0
Leg quarter, roast	100g	92	0	15.4	3.4	0
Light and dark meat, boiled	100g	183	0	29.2	7.3	0
Light and dark meat, raw	100g	121	0	20.5	4.3	0
Light and dark meat, roast	100g	148	0	24.8	5.4	0
Light meat, boiled	100g	163	0	29.7	4.9	0
Light meat, raw	100g	116	0	21.8	3.2	0
Light meat, roast	100g	142	0	26.5	4.0	0
Wing quarter, roast	100g	74	0	12.4	2.7	0
Chicken-based dishes						
Chicken in white sauce, canned	100g	176	3.5	9.5	15.0	0.5
Chicken in white sauce, canned	420g can	780	15.0	40.0	63.0	2.1
Curry	100g	205	3.1	10.2	17.0	0.7
Curry with rice	100g	144	16.9	7.8	5.5	0.8
Duck						
raw	100g	122	0	19.7	4.8	0
roast	100g	189	0	25.3	9.7	0

Food Item	Amount	Kcals	Carb	Prot	Fat	Fibre
Goose						
roast	100g	319	0	29.3	22.4	0
Grouse						
roast	100g	173	0	31.3	5.3	0
roast	1 portion [160g]	277	0	50.1	8.5	0
Ham						
canned	100g	120	0	18.4	5.1	0
Honey roast	100g	108	2.4	18.2	2.9	0
Honey roast	30g slice	32	0.7	5.4	0.9	0
Smoked	100g	94	0.8	17.6	2.3	0
Smoked	30g slice	28	0.2	5.9	0.7	0
Hare						
Stewed	100g	192	0	29.9	8.0	0
Lamb						
Breast, raw	100g	378	0	16.7	34.6	0
Breast, roast	100g	410	0	19.1	37.1	0
Chops, Loin, grilled	100g	355	0	23.5	29.0	0
Chops, Loin, grilled	1 chop [90g]	320	0	21.2	26.1	0
Chops, Loin, raw	100g	377	0	14.6	35.4	0

Food Item	Amount	Kcals	Carb	Prot	Fat	Fibre
Cutlets, grilled	100g	370	0	23.0	30.9	0
Cutlets, grilled	1 cutlet [50g]	185	0	11.5	15.5	0
Cutlets, raw	100g	386	0	14.7	36.3	0
Leg, raw	100g	240	0	17.9	18.7	0
Leg, roast	100g	266	0	26.1	17.9	0
Scrag and neck, raw	100g	316	0	15.6	28.2	0
Scrag and neck, stewed	100g	292	0	25.6	21.1	0
Shoulder, raw	100g	314	0	15.6	28.0	0
Shoulder, roast	100g	316	0	19.9	26.3	0
Lamb-based dishes						
Irish stew	100g	123	9.1	5.3	7.6	1.0
Lamb kheema	100g	328	2.3	14.6	29.1	0.6
Moussaka	100g	184	7.0	9.1	13.6	1.0
Lamb hot pot, frozen	100g	92	7.9	7.9	3.4	1.4
Moussaka, frozen	100g	105	9.9	7.0	4.4	N
Meat-based dishes						
Cottage pie, frozen	100g	110	11.4	5.1	4.7	0.6
Hot pot, home made	100g	114	10.1	9.4	4.5	1.4
Lasagne	100g	102	12.8	5.0	3.8	0.5

Food Item	Amount	Kcals	Carb	Prot	Fat	Fibre
Meat curry	100g	162	9.1	8.5	10.5	1.8
Shepherd's pie	100g	118	8.2	8.0	6.2	0.7
Meat-based products						
Black pudding, fried	100g	305	15.0	12.9	21.9	0.5
Brawn	100g	153	0	12.4	11.5	0
Chopped ham and pork, canned	100g	275	1.4	14.4	23.6	0.3
Cornish pastie	100g	332	31.1	8.0	20.4	1.2
Faggots	100g	268	15.3	11.1	18.5	0.5
Frankfurters	100g	274	3.0	9.5	25.0	0.1
Grillsteaks, grilled	100g	305	0.5	22.1	23.9	trace
Grillsteaks, grilled	1 steak [80g]	244	0.4	17.7	19.1	trace
Haggis, boiled	100g	310	19.2	10.7	21.7	N
Liver pâté	100g	316	1.0	13.1	28.9	trace
Liver pâté, low fat	100g	191	2.8	18.0	12.0	trace
Liver sausage	100g	310	4.3	12.9	26.9	0.5
Luncheon meat, canned	100g	313	5.5	12.6	26.9	0.4
Luncheon meat, canned	20g slice	63	3.3	7.6	16.1	trace
Meat paste	100g	173	3.0	15.2	11.2	0.1

Food Item	Amount	Kcals	Carb	Prot	Fat	Fibre	N
Pepperami	100g	560	1.0	20	52		N
Pepperami	25g stick	140	0.3	5.0	13		N
Polony	100g	281	14.2	9.4	21.1	0.5	
Polony	20g slice	56	2.8	1.9	4.2	0.1	
Pork pie, individual	100g	376	24.9	9.8	27.0	0.9	
Pork pie, individual	1 pie [140g]	526	34.9	13.7	37.8	1.3	
Salami	100g	491	1.9	19.3	45.2	0.1	
Salami	1 slice [17g]	83	0.3	3.3	7.7	trace	
Sausage roll, flaky pastry	100g	477	32.3	7.1	36.4	1.5	
Sausage roll, flaky pastry	1, medium [60g]	286	19.4	46.3	21.8	0.9	
Sausage roll, short pastry	100g	459	37.5	8.0	31.9	1.8	
Sausage roll, short pastry	1, medium [60g]	275	22.5	4.8	19.1	1.1	
Saveloy	100g	262	10.1	9.9	20.5	0.4	
Saveloy	1 medium [65g]	170	6.6	6.4	1.6	0.3	
Steak and kidney pie, individual, pastry top and bottom	1 pie [200g]	646	51.2	18.2	42.4	2.0	
Steak and kidney pie, individual, pastry top and bottom	100g	323	25.6	9.1	21.2	1.0	

Food Item	Amount	Kcals	Carb	Prot	Fat	Fibre
Steak and kidney pie, pastry top	100g	286	15.9	15.2	18.4	0.7
White pudding	100g	450	36.3	7.0	31.8	3.1
Sausages, beef, fried	100g	269	14.9	12.9	18.0	0.8
Sausages, beef, grilled	100g	265	15.2	13.0	17.3	0.8
Sausages, beef, raw	100g	299	11.7	9.6	24.1	0.7
Sausages, pork, fried	100g	317	11.0	13.8	24.5	0.7
Sausages, pork, grilled	100g	318	11.5	13.3	24.6	0.7
Sausages, pork, raw	100g	367	9.5	10.6	32.1	0.6
Sausages, low fat, fried	100g	211	9.1	14.9	13.0	1.2
Sausages, low fat, grilled	100g	229	10.8	16.2	13.8	1.4
Sausages, low fat, raw	100g	166	8.1	12.5	9.5	1.5
Mutton-based dishes						
Mutton biriani	100g	276	25.1	7.5	16.9	1.4
Mutton curry	100g	374	3.9	14.9	33.4	1.0
Offal						
Heart, lamb, raw	100g	119	0	17.1	5.6	0
Heart, ox, raw	100g	108	0	18.9	3.6	0
Heart, ox, stewed	100g	179	0	31.4	5.9	0

Food Item	Amount	Kcals	Carb	Prot	Fat	Fibre
Heart, sheep, roast	100g	237	0	26.1	14.7	0
Kidney, lamb, fried	100g	155	0	24.6	6.3	0
Kidney, lamb, raw	100g	90	0	16.5	2.7	0
Kidney, ox, raw	100g	86	0	15.7	2.6	0
Kidney, ox, stewed	100g	172	0	25.6	7.7	0
Kidney, pig, raw	100g	90	0	16.3	2.7	0
Kidney, pig, stewed	100g	153	0	24.4	6.1	0
Liver, calf, coated in flour and fried	100g	254	7.3	26.9	13.2	0.2
Liver, calf, raw	100g	153	1.9	20.1	7.3	0
Liver, chicken, coated in flour and fried	100g	194	3.4	20.7	10.9	0.2
Liver, chicken, raw	100g	135	0.6	19.1	6.3	0
Liver, lamb, coated in flour and fried	100g	232	3.9	22.9	14.0	0.1
Liver, lamb, raw	100g	179	1.6	20.1	10.3	0
Liver, ox raw	100g	163	2.2	21.1	7.8	0
Liver, ox, coated in flour						

Food Item	Amount	Kcals	Carb	Prot	Fat	Fibre
and stewed	100g	198	3.6	24.8	9.5	trace
Liver, pig, coated in flour and stewed	100g	189	3.6	25.6	8.1	trace
Liver, pig, raw	100g	154	2.1	21.3	6.8	0
Oxtail, stewed	100g	243	0	30.5	13.4	0
Sweetbread, lamb, coated in egg and breadcrumbs and fried	100g	230	5.6	19.4	14.6	0.4
Sweetbread, lamb, raw	100g	131	0	15.3	7.8	0
Tongue, lamb, raw	100g	193	0	15.3	14.6	0
Tongue, ox, boiled	100g	293	0	19.5	23.9	0
Tongue, ox, pickled, raw	100g	220	0	15.7	17.5	0
Tongue, sheep, stewed	100g	289	0	18.2	24.0	0
Tripe, dressed	100g	60	0	9.4	2.5	0
Tripe, dressed, stewed in milk	100g	100	0	14.8	4.5	0
Tripe, dressed, stewed in milk	70g portion	70	0	10.4	3.2	0
Partridge						
roast	100g	212	0	36.7	7.2	0
roast	1 portion [260g]	551	0	95.4	18.7	0

Food Item	Amount	Kcals	Carb	Prot	Fat	Fibre
Pheasant						
roast	100g	213	0	32.2	9.3	0
roast	1 portion [430g]	916	0	138.5	40.0	0
Pigeon						
roast	100g	230	0	27.8	13.2	0
roast	1 portion [115g]	265	0	32.0	15.2	0
Pork						
Belly rashers, grilled	100g	398	0	21.1	34.8	0
Belly rashers, raw	100g	381	0	15.3	35.5	0
Chops, Loin, grilled	100g	332	0	28.5	24.2	0
Chops, Loin, raw	100g	329	0	15.9	29.5	0
Leg, raw	100g	269	0	16.6	22.5	0
Leg, roast	100g	286	0	26.9	19.8	0
Trotters and tails, boiled	100g	280	0	19.8	22.3	0
Rabbit						
raw	100g	124	0	21.9	4.0	0
stewed	100g	179	0	27.3	7.7	0
Tongue						
canned	100g	213	0	16.0	16.5	0

Food Item	Amount	Kcals	Carb	Prot	Fat	Fibre
Turkey						
Dark meat, raw	100g	114	0	20.3	3.6	0
Dark meat, roast	100g	148	0	27.8	4.1	0
Light and dark meat, raw	100g	107	0	21.9	2.2	0
Light and dark meat, roast	100g	140	0	28.8	2.7	0
Light meat, raw	100g	103	0	23.2	1.1	0
Light meat, roast	100g	132	0	29.8	1.4	0
Turkey-based product						
Turkey with ham	100g	123	2.2	19.2	4.1	0
Turkey with ham	30g slice	37	0.7	5.8	1.2	0
Veal						
Cutlet, coated in egg and breadcrumbs and fried	100g	215	4.4	31.4	8.1	0.3
Fillet, raw	100g	109	0	21.1	2.7	0
Fillet, roast	100g	230	0	31.6	11.5	0
Venison						
Haunch, roast	100g	198	0	35.0	6.4	0
Haunch, roast	120g portion	238	0	42.0	7.7	0

Soups, Sauces and Miscellaneous

Food Item	Amount	Kcals	Carb	Prot	Fat	Fibre
Chutney						
Apple	100g	201	52.2	0.9	0.2	1.8
Apple	1 heaped tsp [15g]	30	7.8	0.1	trace	0.3
Mango	100g	285	49.5	0.4	10.9	1.4
Mango	1 heaped tsp [15g]	43	7.4	0.1	1.6	0.2
Tomato	100g	161	40.9	1.2	0.4	1.9
Tomato	1 heaped tsp [15g]	24	6.1	0.2	0.1	0.3
Miscellaneous						
Baking powder	100g	163	37.8	5.2	trace	0
Baking powder	1 level tsp	7	1.5	0.2	trace	0
Bovril	100g	169	2.9	38.0	0.7	0
Bovril	portion [3g]	5	0.1	1.1	trace	0
Bovril	1 level tsp [9g]	15	0.3	3.4	trace	0
Gelatine	100g	338	0	84	0	0
Gravy granules, made with water	100g	462	40.6	4.4	32.5	trace

Food Item	Amount	Kcals	Carb	Prot	Fat	Fibre
Marmite	100g	172	1.8	39.7	0.7	0
Marmite	portion [3g]	5	0.1	1.2	trace	0
Marmite	1 level tsp [9g]	15	0.2	3.6	0.1	0
Mustard, smooth	100g	139	9.7	7.1	8.2	N
Mustard, smooth	1 level tsp [8g]	11	0.8	0.6	0.7	N
Mustard, wholegrain	100g	140	4.2	8.2	10.2	4.9
Mustard, wholegrain	1 level tsp	11	0.3	0.7	0.8	0.4
Oxo cubes	100g	229	12.0	38.3	3.4	0
Oxo cubes	1 cube [7g]	16	0.8	2.7	0.2	0
Salt	100g	0	0	0	0	0
Salt	1 tsp	0	0	0	0	0
Vinegar	100g	4	0.6	0.4	0	0
Vinegar	1 tbsp [15g]	1	0.1	0.1	0	0
Yeast, baker's compressed	100g	5	1.1	11.4	0.4	6.2
Yeast, dried	100g	169	3.5	35.6	1.5	19.7
Pickle						
Sweet	100g	134	34.4	0.6	0.3	1.5
Sweet	1 heaped tsp [15g]	20	5.2	trace	trace	0.2

Food Item	Amount	Kcals	Carb	Prot	Fat	Fibre
Salad dressing						
French dressing	100g	649	0.1	0.3	72.1	0
Mayonnaise	100g	691	1.7	1.1	75.6	0
Salad cream	100g	348	16.7	1.5	31.0	N
Salad cream, reduced calorie	100g	194	9.4	1.0	17.2	N
Sauce						
Barbecue	100g	75	12.2	1.8	1.8	N
Bread sauce, made with semi-skimmed milk	100g	93	12.8	4.3	3.1	0.6
Bread sauce, made with whole milk	100g	110	12.6	4.2	5.1	0.6
Brown sauce, bottled	100g	99	25.2	1.1	0	0.7
Cheese sauce, made with semi-skimmed milk	100g	179	9.1	8.1	12.6	0.2
Cheese sauce, made with whole milk	100g	197	8.0	14.6	14.5	0.2
Cheese sauce, packet mix, made with semi-skimmed milk	100g	90	9.5	5.4	3.8	N

Food Item	Amount	Kcals	Carb	Prot	Fat	Fibre
Cheese sauce, packet mix, made with whole milk	100g	110	9.3	5.3	6.1	N
Cook-in sauces, canned, average	100g	43	8.3	1.1	0.8	N
Curry sauce, canned	100g	78	7.1	1.5	5.0	N
Horseradish sauce	100g	153	17.9	2.5	8.4	2.5
Mint sauce	100g	87	21.5	1.6	trace	N
Onion sauce, made with semi-skimmed milk	100g	86	8.4	2.9	5.0	0.6
Onion sauce, made with whole milk	100g	99	8.3	2.8	6.5	0.6
Pasta sauce, tomato based	100g	47	6.9	2.0	1.5	1.1
Soy sauce	100g	64	8.3	8.7	0	0
Soy sauce	1 tsp [5g]	3	0.4	0.4	0	0
Tomato ketchup	100g	98	24.0	2.1	trace	0.9
White sauce, savoury, made with semi-skimmed milk	100g	128	11.1	4.2	7.8	0.3
White sauce, savoury, mad with whole milk	100g	150	10.9	4.1	10.3	0.3

Food Item	Amount	Kcals	Carb	Prot	Fat	Fibre
White sauce, sweet, made with semi-skimmed milk	100g	150	18.8	3.9	7.2	0.2
White sauce, sweet, made with whole milk	100g	170	18.6	3.8	9.5	0.2
Soup						
Chicken noodle, dried, ready to serve	100g	20	3.7	0.8	0.3	0.2
Cream of chicken, canned, ready to serve	100g	58	4.5	1.7	3.8	N
Cream of chicken, condensed, canned	100g	98	6.0	2.6	7.2	N
Cream of chicken, condensed, diluted, ready to serve	100g	49	3.0	1.3	3.6	N
Cream of mushroom soup, canned, ready to serve	100g	53	3.9	1.1	3.8	N
Cream of tomato, canned, ready to serve	100g	55	5.9	0.8	3.3	0.6
Cream of tomato, condensed, canned	100g	123	14.6	1.7	6.8	1.2

Food Item	Amount	Kcals	Carb	Prot	Fat	Fibre
Cream of tomato, condensed, diluted, ready to serve	100g	62	7.3	0.9	3.4	0.6
Instant soup powder, average, made with water, ready to serve	100g	64	10.5	1.1	2.3	N
Lentil, home-made	100g	99	12.7	4.4	3.8	2.0
Low-calorie, average, canned	100g	20	4.0	0.9	0.2	N
Minestrone, dried, ready to serve	100g	298	47.6	10.1	8.8	0.5
Oxtail, canned, ready to serve	100g	44	5.1	2.4	1.7	N
Oxtail, dried, ready to serve	100g	27	3.9	1.4	0.8	0.3
Tomato, dried, ready to serve	100g	31	6.3	0.6	0.5	0.3
Vegetable, canned, ready to serve	100g	37	6.7	1.5	0.7	1.5

Desserts

Food Item	Amount	Kcals	Carb	Prot	Fat	Fibre
Blackcurrant pie						
home-made, pastry top & bottom	100g	262	34.5	3.1	13.3	4.8
Bread pudding						
home-made	100g	297	49.7	5.9	9.6	3.0
Cheesecake						
frozen, with fruit	100g	242	33.0	5.7	10.6	0.9
individual, fruit purée topping	100g	274	32.4	5.8	13.5	N
Christmas pudding						
home-made	100g	291	49.5	4.6	9.7	2.7
retail	100g	329	56.3	3.0	11.8	3.4
Creamed Rice						
canned	100g	91	15.2	3.4	1.8	0.2
canned	425g can	387	64.6	14.5	7.7	0.9
Creamed Sago						
canned	100g	82	13.0	2.9	1.8	0.2

Food Item	Amount	Kcals	Carb	Prot	Fat	Fibre
canned	425g can	349	55.3	12.3	7.7	0.9
Creamed Semolina						
canned	100g	84	13.2	3.6	1.9	0.2
canned	425g can	357	56.1	15.3	8.1	0.9
Creme Caramel						
individual	100g	109	20.6	3.0	2.2	N
Custard						
Devon, canned	100g	102	15.8	2.8	3.1	trace
Devon, canned	425g can	434	67.2	11.0	13.2	trace
home-made, made with skimmed milk	100g	79	16.8	3.8	0.1	trace
home-made, made with whole milk	100g	117	16.6	3.7	4.5	trace
low-fat, canned	100g	75	12.5	3.0	1.4	trace
low-fat, canned	425g can	319	53.1	12.8	6.0	trace
Frozen dessert						
Arctic roll	100g	200	33.3	4.1	6.6	0.8
Chocolate nut sundae	100g	278	34.2	3.0	15.3	0.2
Viennetta	100g	272	27.6	3.8	16.4	trace

Food Item	Amount	Kcals	Carb	Prot	Fat	Fibre
Viennetta	50g slice	136	13.8	1.9	8.2	trace
Frozen ice cream dessert	100g	227	22.8	3.3	14.2	trace
Fruit crumble						
Home-made	100g	198	34.0	2.0	6.9	2.2
Home-made with wholemeal	100g	193	31.7	2.6	7.1	3.0
Fruit pie						
pastry top and bottom	100g	262	34.5	3.1	13.3	2.2
Fruit pie filling						
Apple and blackberry, canned	100g	92	24.1	0.3	trace	1.6
Black cherry, canned	100g	98	25.8	0.3	trace	1.6
Ice cream						
Choc ice	100g	277	28.1	3.5	17.5	trace
Cornetto	75g cone	195	25.8	2.8	9.7	trace
Dairy, vanilla	100g	194	24.4	3.6	9.8	trace
Dairy, vanilla	60g scoop	116	14.6	2.2	5.9	trace
Flavoured	100g	179	24.7	3.5	8.0	trace
Flavoured	60g scoop	107	14.8	2.1	4.8	trace
Luxury, full cream, vanilla	100g	237	17.4	4.4	16.6	trace

Food Item	Amount	Kcals	Carb	Prot	Fat	Fibre
Non-dairy, flavoured	100g	166	23.2	3.1	7.4	trace
Non-dairy, flavoured	60g scoop	100	13.9	1.9	4.4	trace
Non-dairy, vanilla	100g	178	23.1	3.2	8.7	trace
Non-dairy, vanilla	60g scoop	107	13.9	1.9	5.2	trace
Ice cream mix	100g	182	25.1	4.1	7.9	trace
Ice cream wafers	100g	342	78.8	10.1	0.7	trace
Jelly						
Fruit-flavoured, before dilution	100g	280	69.7	4.7	trace	0
Lemon meringue pie						
Home-made	100g	319	45.9	4.5	14.4	0.8
Meringue						
Home-made	100g	379	95.4	5.3	trace	0
Home-made	1 average [8g]	30	7.6	0.4	trace	0
Mousse						
Chocolate, individual	100g	139	19.9	4.0	5.4	0
Chocolate, individual	60g carton	83	11.9	2.4	3.2	0
Fruit, individual	100g	137	18.0	4.5	5.7	trace
Fruit, individual	60g carton	82.2	10.8	2.7	3.4	trace

Food Item	Amount	Kcals	Carb	Prot	Fat	Fibre
Pancakes						
Sweet, made with whole milk	100g	301	35.0	5.9	16.2	0.9
Pie						
With pie filling	100g	273	34.6	3.2	14.5	2.1
Rice pudding						
Average, canned	100g	89	14.0	3.4	2.5	0.2
With sultanas and nutmeg	100g	101	17.1	3.3	2.6	0.4
Sorbet						
Lemon, home-made	100g	131	34.2	0.9	trace	0
Lemon, home-made	60g scoop	79	20.5	0.5	trace	0
Sponge pudding						
Home-made	100g	340	45.3	5.8	16.3	1.2
Steamed sponge pudding						
Chocolate, with chocolate sauce, canned	100g	299	51.2	2.6	9.3	0.6
Treacle, canned	100g	301	51.4	2.2	9.6	0.7
with jam, canned	100g	299	49.8	2.6	9.9	0.6

Food Item	Amount	Kcals	Carb	Prot	Fat	Fibre
Trifle						
Fruit cocktail, individual	100g	182	23.1	2.5	2.6	0.5
Home-made	100g	160	22.3	3.6	6.3	0.5
Home-made, with cream	100g	166	19.5	2.4	9.2	0.5
Milk chocolate, individual	100g	282	25.1	4.7	18.2	0.5
Raspberry, individual	100g	173	21.1	2.5	8.7	0.5
Yoghurt						
Greek, strained	100g	115	2.0	6.4	9.1	0
Low-fat, fruit	100g	90	17.9	4.1	0.7	trace
Low-fat, fruit	150g pot	135	26.9	6.2	1.1	trace
Low-fat, plain	100g	56	7.5	5.1	0.8	0
Low-fat, plain	150g pot	84	11.3	7.7	1.2	0
Very low-fat, fruit	100g	45	6.3	5.2	0.1	trace
Very low-fat, fruit	150g pot	55	7.9	6.5	0.1	trace
Whole milk, fruit	100g	105	15.7	5.1	2.8	trace
Whole milk, fruit	150g pot	158	23.6	7.7	4.2	trace
Whole milk, plain	100g	79	7.8	5.7	3.0	0
Whole milk, plain	150g pot	119	11.7	8.6	4.5	0

Snacks

Food Item	Amount	Kcals	Carb	Prot	Fat	Fibre
Chocolate Confectionery						
Aero	100g	522	58.3	7.7	28.7	N
Aero	standard bar [46g]	252	26.7	4.0	14.4	N
Boost	100g	515	60.1	6.2	27.6	N
Boost	standard bar [57g]	295	34.3	3.5	15.7	N
Bounty bar	100g	473	58.3	4.8	26.1	N
Bounty bar	mini bar [30g]	142	17.5	1.44	7.8	N
Chocolate cream	100g	425	72.6	2.7	13.7	N
Chocolate cream	standard bar [50g]	215	36.3	1.4	6.9	N
Chocolate, milk	100g	529	59.4	8.4	30.3	N
Chocolate, plain	100g	525	64.8	4.7	29.2	N
Chocolate, white	100g	529	58.3	8.0	30.9	N
Chocolates, fancy and filled [assorted]	100g	460	73.3	4.1	18.8	trace
Creme egg	100g	385	58.0	4.1	16.8	trace
Creme egg	1 egg [39g]	150	22.6	1.6	6.6	trace

Food Item	Amount	Kcals	Carb	Prot	Fat	Fibre
Crunchie	100g	460	72.7	4.6	19.1	N
Crunchie	standard bar [35g]	195	30.5	1.9	8.0	N
Dairy Milk	medium bar [54g]	285	30.7	4.3	15.9	N
Dairy Milk	100g	525	56.8	7.8	29.4	N
Flake	100g	505	58.4	8.2	28.5	N
Flake	standard bar [35g]	170	19.9	2.8	9.7	N
Kit Kat	100g	499	60.5	8.2	26.6	N
Kit Kat	2 bars [20g]	100	12.1	1.6	5.3	N
Mars Bar	100g	441	66.5	5.3	18.9	trace
Mars Bar	1 mini bar [20g]	88	13.3	1.1	3.8	trace
Mars Bar	standard bar [68g]	300	9.0	0.7	2.6	trace
Milky Bar	100g	549	55.6	8.4	32.5	trace
Milky Bar	1 medium bar [20g]	110	11.1	1.7	6.4	trace
Milky Way	100g	397	63.4	4.4	15.8	trace
Milky Way	standard bar [55g]	218	34.8	2.4	8.7	trace
Smarties	100g	456	73.9	5.4	17.5	N
Smarties	1 tube [36g]	164	26.6	1.9	6.3	N
Topic	100g	497	56.7	7.4	26.7	N
Topic	1 bar [54g]	268	30.6	4.0	14.4	N

Food Item	Amount	Kcals	Carb	Prot	Fat	Fibre
Turkish Delight	100g	370	69.0	1.6	7.7	N
Turkish Delight	1 bar [51g]	190	37.8	0.8	3.9	N
Non-chocolate Confectionery						
Boiled sweets	100g	327	87.3	trace	trace	0
Fruit Gums	100g	172	44.8	1.0	0	0
Fruit Gums	1 tube [33g]	57	14.8	0.3	0	0
Liquorice Allsorts	1 small bag [56g]	175	41.5	2.2	1.2	N
Liquorice Allsorts	100g	313	74.1	3.9	2.2	N
Opal Fruits	100g	411	85.3	0.3	7.6	0
Opal Fruits	1 pack [56g]	230	47.7	0.2	4.3	0
Pastilles, assorted	100g	253	61.9	5.2	0	0
Peppermints, assorted	100g	392	102.2	0.5	0.7	0
Popcorn, candied	100g	480	77.6	2.1	20.0	2.9
Popcorn, plain	100g	592	48.6	6.2	42.8	N
Skittles	100g	383	91.5	0.3	4.3	0
Skittles	1 pack [60g]	230	54.9	0.2	2.6	0
Toffees, mixed	100g	430	71.1	2.1	17.2	0
Turkish Delight	100g	295	77.9	0.6	0	0

Food Item	Amount	Kcals	Carb	Prot	Fat	Fibre
Turkish Delight	50g bar	198	38.9	0.3	0	0
Savoury Snacks						
Bombay mix	100g	503	35.1	18.8	32.9	6.2
Cheddars	100g	534	52.9	11.3	30.2	2.3
Corn snacks	100g	519	54.3	7.0	31.9	1.0
Peanuts and raisins	100g	435	37.5	15.3	26.0	6.8
Potato crisps, assorted	100g	546	49.3	5.6	37.6	4.3
Potato crisps, assorted	28g bag	153	13.8	1.6	10.5	1.2
Potato crisps, low fat, assorted	100g	456	63.0	6.6	21.5	6.3
Potato crisps, low fat, assorted	28g bag	128	17.6	1.8	6.0	1.8
Potato crisps, thick cut, old style	100g	485	42.7	6.9	31.0	13.9
Potato Hoops	100g	523	58.5	3.9	32.0	N
Skips [KP]	100g	512	59.8	4.2	28.4	N
Skips [KP]	18g bag	92	10.8	0.8	5.1	N
Tortilla Chips	100g	459	60.1	7.6	22.6	4.1
Trail Mix	100g	432	37.2	9.1	28.5	4.3
Twiglets	100g	383	62.0	11.3	11.7	N
Wotsits	100g	545	52.4	9.4	33.1	N
Wotsits	21g bag	115	11.0	2.0	7.0	N

Sugar, Syrups and Preserves

Food Item	Amount	Kcals	Carb	Prot	Fat	Fibre
Preserves						
Jam, fruit	100g	261	69.0	0.6	0	0
Jam, fruit	1 heaped tsp [18g]	47	12.4	0.1	0	0
Jam, stone fruit	100g	261	69.3	0.4	0	0.9
Jam, stone fruit	1 heaped tsp [18g]	47	12.5	0.1	0	0.2
Jam, reduced sugar	100g	123	31.9	0.5	0	0.9
Jam, reduced sugar	1 heaped tsp [18g]	22	5.7	0.1	0	0.2
Lemon curd	100g	283	62.7	0.6	5.1	0.2
Lemon curd	1 heaped tsp [18g]	51	11.3	0.1	0.9	trace
Marmalade	100g	261	69.5	0.1	0	0.6
Marmalade	1 heaped tsp [18g]	47	12.5	trace	0	0.1
Mincemeat	100g	274	62.1	0.6	4.3	3.0
Spread						
Chocolate nut	100g	549	60.5	6.2	33.0	1.2
Chocolate nut	1 heaped tsp [16g]	88	9.7	1.0	5.3	0.2

Food Item	Amount	Kcals	Carb	Prot	Fat	Fibre
Honey	100g	288	76.4	0.4	0	0
Honey	1 heaped tsp [17g]	49	13.0	0.1	0	0
Honey & comb	100g	281	74.4	0.6	4.6	0
Sugar						
Demerara	100g	394	104.5	0.5	0	0
Demerara	1 tsp [20g]	79	20.9	0.1	0	0
Demerara	1 level tsp [4g]	16	4.2	trace	0	0
Glucose liquid	100g	318	84.7	trace	0	0
White	100g	394	105.0	trace	0	0
White	1 tbsp [20g]	79	21.0	trace	0	0
White	1 cube [5g]	20	5.3	trace	0	0
Treacle						
Black	100g	257	67.2	1.2	0	0
Syrup						
Golden	100g	298	79.0	0.3	0	0

Fats and Oils

Food Item	Amount	Kcals	Carb	Prot	Fat	Fibre
Animal fat						
Compound cooking fat	100g	894	trace	trace	99.3	0
Dripping, beef	100g	891	trace	trace	99.0	0
Lard	100g	891	trace	trace	99.0	0
Suet, shredded	100g	826	12.1	trace	86.7	0.6
Ghee						
Butter	100g	898	trace	trace	99.8	0
Palm	100g	897	trace	trace	99.7	0
Vegetable	100g	898	trace	trace	99.8	0
Oil						
Coconut oil	100g	899	0	trace	99.9	0
Cod liver oil	100g	899	0	trace	99.9	0
Corn oil	100g	899	0	trace	99.9	0
Cottonseed oil	100g	899	0	trace	99.9	0
Extra virgin olive oil	100g	898	0	trace	99.8	0

Food Item	Amount	Kcals	Carb	Prot	Fat	Fibre
Olive oil	100g	899	0	trace	99.9	0
Palm oil	100g	899	0	trace	99.9	0
Peanut oil	100g	899	0	trace	99.9	0
Rapeseed oil	100g	899	0	trace	99.9	0
Safflower oil	100g	899	0	trace	99.9	0
Sesame oil	100g	881	0	0.2	99.7	0
Soya oil	100g	899	0	trace	99.9	0
Sunflower seed oil	100g	899	0	trace	99.9	0
Vegetable oil, blended, average	100g	899	0	trace	99.9	0
Wheatgerm oil	100g	899	0	trace	99.9	0
Spreading fat						
Butter	100g	737	trace	0.5	81.7	0
Dairy/fat spread	100g	662	trace	0.4	73.4	0
Low fat spread	100g	390	0.5	5.8	40.5	0
Margarine, hard, animal and vegetable fat	100g	739	1.0	0.2	81.6	0
Margarine, hard, vegetable fat only	100g	739	1.0	0.2	81.6	0
Margarine, soft, animal and vegetable fat	100g	739	1.0	0.2	81.6	0

Food Item	Amount	Kcals	Carb	Prot	Fat	Fibre
Margarine, soft, vegetable fat only	100g	739	1.0	0.2	81.6	0
Margarine, polyunsaturated	100g	739	1.0	0.2	81.6	0
Very low fat spread	100g	273	3.6	8.3	25.0	0

Alcoholic and Non-alcoholic Beverages

Food Item	Amount	Kcals	Carb	Prot	Fat	Fibre
Ale						
Bottled, brown	100ml	28	3	trace	0	0
Bottled, brown	1 pint	159	17	trace	0	0
Bottled, pale	100ml	32	2	trace	0	0
Bottled, pale	1 pint	182	11.4	trace	0	0
Beer						
Bitter, canned	100ml	32	2.3	trace	0	0
Bitter, canned	1 pint	182	13.1	trace	0	0
Bitter, draught	100ml	32	2.3	trace	0	0
Bitter, draught	1 pint	182	13.1	trace	0	0
Bitter, keg	100ml	31	2.3	trace	0	0
Bitter, keg	1 pint	176	13.1	trace	0	0
Mild, draught	100ml	25	1.6	trace	0	0
Mild, draught	1 pint	142	9.1	trace	0	0
Stout	100ml	37	4.2	trace	0	0

Food Item	Amount	Kcals	Carb	Prot	Fat	Fibre
Stout	1 pint	210	23.5	trace	0	0
Stout, extra	100ml	39	2.1	trace	0	0
Stout, extra	1 pint	222	11.9	trace	0	0
Cider						
Dry	100ml	36	2.6	trace	0	0
Dry	1 pint	204	14.8	trace	0	0
Sweet	100ml	42	4.3	trace	0	0
Sweet	1 pint	238	24.4	trace	0	0
Vintage	100ml	101	7.3	trace	0	0
Vintage	1 pint	573	41.5	trace	0	0
Fortified Wine						
Port	30ml	47	3.6	trace	0	0
Sherry, dry	30ml	35	0.5	trace	0	0
Sherry, medium	30ml	35	1.0	trace	0	0
Sherry, sweet	30ml	43	2	trace	0	0
Lager						
Bottled	100ml	29	1.5	trace	0	0
Bottled	1 pint	165	8.5	trace	0	0

Food Item	Amount	Kcals	Carb	Prot	Fat	Fibre
Spirits						
Brandy, 40% proof	30ml	65	trace	trace	0	0
Gin, 40% proof	30ml	65	trace	trace	0	0
Rum, 40% proof	30ml	65	trace	trace	0	0
Vodka, 40% proof	30ml	65	trace	trace	0	0
Whisky, 40% proof	30ml	65	trace	trace	0	0
Wine						
Red	100ml	68	0.3	trace	0	0
Red	1 bottle [750ml]	510	2.3	trace	0	0
Red	1 glass [120ml]	82	0.4	trace	0	0
Rosé, medium	100ml	71	2.5	trace	0	0
Rosé, medium	1 bottle [750ml]	533	18.8	trace	0	0
Rosé, medium	1 glass [120ml]	85	3.0	trace	0	0
White, dry	100ml	66	0.6	trace	0	0
White, dry	1 bottle [750ml]	495	4.5	trace	0	0
White, dry	1 glass [120ml]	79	0.7	trace	0	0
White, medium	100ml	75	3.4	trace	0	0
White, medium	1 bottle [750ml]	563	25.5	trace	0	0

Food Item	Amount	Kcals	Carb	Prot	Fat	Fibre
White, medium	1 glass [120ml]	90	4.1	trace	0	0
White, sparkling	100ml	76	1.4	trace	0	0
White, sparkling	1 bottle [750ml]	570	10.5	trace	0	0
White, sparkling	1 glass [120ml]	91	1.7	trace	0	0
White, sweet	100ml	94	5.9	trace	0	0
White, sweet	1 bottle [750ml]	705	44.3	trace	0	0
White, sweet	1 glass [120ml]	113	53.2	trace	0	0
Bournvita						
Semi-skimmed milk	100g	58	7.8	3.5	1.6	trace
Semi-skimmed milk	1 mug [260g]	151	20.3	9.1	4.2	trace
Whole milk	100g	76	7.6	3.4	3.8	trace
Whole milk	1 mug [260g]	198	19.8	8.9	9.9	trace
Carbonated drink						
Coca-cola	100g	36	10.5	trace	0	0
Coca-cola	1 can [330g]	119	5.0	trace	0	0
Lemonade, bottled	100g	21	5.6	trace	0	0
Lemonade, bottled	1 glass [200g]	42	11.2	trace	0	0
Cocoa						
Semi-skimmed milk	100g	57	7.0	3.5	1.9	0.2

Food Item	Amount	Kcals	Carb	Prot	Fat	Fibre
Semi-skimmed milk	1 mug [260g]	148	18.2	22.9	4.9	0.5
Whole milk	100g	76	6.8	3.4	4.2	0.2
Whole milk	1 mug [260g]	198	17.7	8.8	10.9	0.5
Coffee						
Instant, 30g of whole milk	1 mug	22	1.6	1.3	1.2	0
Instant, without milk or sugar	1 mug [260g]	2	0.2	0.3	0	0
Coffeemate						
Powder	100g	540	57.3	2.7	34.9	0
Powder	portion [6g]	32	3.4	0.2	2.1	0
Complan						
Sweet, water	100g	96	13.4	4.5	3.1	trace
Sweet, water	1 mug [260g]	250	34.8	11.7	8.1	trace
Sweet, whole milk	100g	145	16.9	6.9	6.1	trace
Sweet, whole milk	1 mug [260g]	377	43.9	17.9	15.9	trace
Cordial						
Lime juice cordial, undiluted	100g	112	29.8	0.1	0	0
Lime juice cordial, undiluted	1 glass [40g]	45	11.9	trace	0	0
Rosehip syrup, undiluted	100g	232	4.8	trace	0	0
Rosehip syrup, undiluted	1 glass [40g]	93	1.9	trace	0	0

Food Item	Amount	Kcals	Carb	Prot	Fat	Fibre
Drinking chocolate						
Semi-skimmed milk	100g	71	10.8	3.5	1.9	trace
Semi-skimmed milk	1 mug [260g]	185	28.1	9.1	4.9	trace
Whole milk	100g	90	10.6	3.4	4.1	trace
Whole milk	1 mug [260g]	234	27.6	8.8	10.7	trace
Horlicks						
Instant, water	100g	51	10.1	2.4	0.5	trace
Instant, water	1 mug [260g]	133	26.6	6.2	1.3	trace
Semi-skimmed milk	100g	81	12.9	4.3	1.9	trace
Semi-skimmed milk	1 mug [260g]	211	33.5	11.2	4.9	trace
Whole milk	100g	99	12.7	4.2	3.9	trace
Whole milk	1 mug [260g]	257	33.0	10.9	10.1	trace
Juice						
Apple juice, unsweetened	100g	38	9.9	0.1	0.1	trace
Apple juice, unsweetened	1 glass [200g]	76	328	0.2	0.2	trace
Grape juice, unsweetened	100g	46	11.7	0.3	0.1	trace
Grape juice, unsweetened	1 glass [200g]	92	23.4	0.6	0.2	trace
Grapefruit juice, unsweetened	100g	33	8.3	0.4	0.1	trace
Grapefruit juice, unsweetened	1 glass [200g]	66	16.6	0.8	0.2	trace
Lemon juice, unsweetened	100g	7	1.6	0.3	trace	0.1

Food Item	Amount	Kcals	Carb	Prot	Fat	Fibre
Lemon juice, unsweetened	1 tbsp [15g]	1	0.2	trace	trace	trace
Orange juice, unsweetened	100g	36	8.8	0.5	0.1	0.1
Orange juice, unsweetened	1 glass [200g]	72	17.6	1.0	0.2	0.2
Pineapple juice, unsweetened	100g	41	10.5	0.3	0.1	trace
Pineapple juice, unsweetened	1 glass [200g]	82	21.0	0.6	0.2	trace
Tomato juice	100g	14	3.0	0.8	trace	0.6
Tomato juice	1 glass [200g]	28	6.0	1.6	trace	0.2
Milk shake						
Semi-skimmed milk	1 glass [200g]	138	22.6	6.4	3.2	trace
Semi-skimmed milk	100g	69	11.3	3.2	1.6	trace
Whole milk	100g	87	11.1	3.1	3.7	trace
Whole milk	1 glass [200g]	174	22.2	6.2	7.4	trace
Thick, take-away	100g	90	13.2	2.9	3.2	trace
Mixers						
Ginger ale	100g	23	5.7	trace	trace	0
Ginger ale	1 glass [200g]	46	11.4	trace	trace	0
Ginger ale, low-calorie	100g	1.8	0.04	trace	trace	0
Ginger ale, low-calorie	220g	3.6	0.08	trace	trace	0
Tonic water	100g	23	5.4	trace	trace	0

Food Item	Amount	Kcals	Carb	Prot	Fat	Fibre
Tonic water	1 glass [200g]	46	10.8	trace	trace	0
Tonic water, low-calorie	100g	0.8	trace	trace	trace	0
Tonic water, low-calorie	1 glass [200g]	1.6	trace	trace	trace	0
Ovaltine						
Semi-skimmed milk	100g	79	13.0	3.9	1.7	trace
Semi-skimmed milk	1 mug [260g]	205	33.8	10.1	4.4	trace
Whole milk	100g	97	12.9	3.8	3.8	trace
Whole milk	1 mug [260g]	252	4.9	9.9	9.9	trace
Squash						
Orange drink, undiluted	100g	107	28.5	trace	0	0
Orange drink, undiluted	1 glass [40g]	43	11.4	trace	0	0
Ribena	100g	228	60.8	0.1	0	0
Ribena	1 glass [40g]	91	24.3	trace	0	0
Tea						
No milk or sugar	100g	trace	trace	0.1	trace	0
No milk or sugar	1 cup [200g]	trace	trace	0.2	trace	0
With 30g of whole milk	1 cup [200g]	20	1.4	1.2	1.2	0